THE LAST SUMMER
May to September 1914

THE
LAST SUMMER

May to September
1914

Kirsty McLeod

St. Martin's Press
New York

Library of Congress Cataloging in Publication Data

McLeod, Kirsty.
    The last summer.

    1. World War, 1914-1918—Fiction.   I. Title.
PR6063.C57L3   1984   823'.914   84-2111
ISBN 0-312-47157-2

First Published in Great Britain by William Collins Sons
& Co. Ltd.

First U.S. Edition

10 9 8 7 6 5 4 3 2 1

For Christopher

ILLUSTRATIONS

ACKNOWLEDGEMENTS

My thanks are many and various. In the first place, at the very beginning of my research, Roderick Suddaby and his staff in the Department of Documents at the Imperial War Museum pointed me in the right direction. Hilda French, now Mrs Hilda Felstead, Mrs Edward Pleydell-Bouverie (Pearl Barrington Crake), Lady (Violet) Graham, Mark Hayler, the late Brigadier Cyril Drummond and the late Bessie Ellis were all most generous with their time and hospitality. So were Captain Ulric Nisbet and his wife, Christine. Captain Nisbet also lent me books and photographs and allowed me to quote extensively from his Diaries and Memories of the Great War; Recollections of a Very Young Man at the Beginning of the Great War, and Old School Tie, Recollections of Marlborough before the First World War (published in *The Marlburian*, summer 1964). Lady Diana Cooper saw me twice and lent me her photograph albums.

I have also spoken to many people who, if they were not written about at length directly, nevertheless contributed valuable background material. Among them were: Sir Roger Chance; Geoffrey Barrington-Chance; Captain Eric Wheeler Bush, RN; the late Captain Percy Snelling (thanks, too, to his family, Diana and Ewart Parsons); H. G. R. Williams; Mrs Edith Reid; ex-Lieutenant Richard Fletcher; Mrs Lucy Holman; Miss Gabrielle West; the late Mrs Margery Hassell; the late Ronald Brooks; the late Tom Elliott; the late Lady Hardinge of Penshurst (thanks also to Dr John Elliott who contacted her); T. A. Silver, who answered countless questions most patiently by letter. Finally, thanks to Mrs Nigel West for putting me in touch with Bessie Ellis.

I am grateful also to the Trustees of the Imperial War Museum for allowing me access to a number of collections. I have made particular use of the following, which can be consulted in the museum's Department of Documents: **Captain W. T. Colyer; Brigadier C. A. F. Drummond; M. H. C. Hayler; Captain H. U. S. Nisbet; T. A. Silver.**

Acknowledgements are due to those mentioned below for permission to quote from copyright material: Harrap Ltd. (*A Shropshire Lad* by A. E. Housman); George Rainbird (*The Edwardians* by J. B. Priestley); David Higham Associates (*Great Morning* by Osbert Sitwell, *Remember And Be Glad* by Cynthia Asquith); Robert Graves (*Goodbye to All That* by Robert Graves); Lady Diana Cooper (*The Rainbow Comes and Goes*); the literary estate of Isaac Rosenberg and Chatto & Windus Ltd. (*August 1914* from

The Collected Poems of Isaac Rosenberg); Faber & Faber *(MCMXIV* from *The Whitsun Weddings* by Philip Larkin, *The Letters of Rupert Brooke* ed. Geoffrey Keynes); The Hogarth Press *(Rupert Brooke* from *Moments of Being* by Virginia Woolf: ed. Mary Lyon); George Sassoon *(The Weald of Youth* by Siegfried Sassoon).

I

The Golden Age

UPPINGHAM SCHOOL'S last speech-day before the Great War took place over a stiflingly hot weekend in mid-July 1914. Saturday, the hottest day of all, found parents, friends and boys clustered thick on the Headmaster's lawn, where the afternoon sun blazed down on beds of crimson and orange roses. Among the sea of straw boaters and shady hats, another in pink silk went unnoticed, and young Vera Brittain stood for some time hiding beneath its lace-trimmed brim, engrossed in private conversation with one of Uppingham's star pupils and senior prefects. But then her brother's Housemaster intervened, breaking up the tête à tête with forced and disapproving jocularity, and bearing Vera off to the more suitable ambience of the ladies' tea tent.

The young man's name was Roland Leighton. He was nineteen, fair-haired and stocky, and in enviable possession of a classics scholarship to Merton College, Oxford, which he was due to take up that autumn. Earlier in the day, Vera had watched him win six out of seven of the year's classics prizes, and then re-tread the length of the school hall to accept the special prize for English Essay. Earlier still, she had lined the route, as in his field uniform and with his colour sergeant's stripes, he joined her brother and a squad of serious-faced teenagers in the march-past of Uppingham Officers' Training Corps. It was an impressive sight and Vera, already strongly attracted to Roland, resolved not to tease him about it. She was conscious of how much it meant to him, and indeed to her brother Edward and his friend Victor, the inseparable trio christened ironically by Roland's writer mother 'The Three Musketeers'.

To the watching parents and friends the military manoeuvres on Uppingham's Middle Field signified nothing more sinister than healthy boyish outdoor exercise, a foretaste of the Public Schools Camp which was to assemble at Aldershot at the beginning of

August in a fortnight's time. After that, a thought which over-shadowed Vera's homeward journey and made her cross and un-approachable even with her patient mother, Roland and Edward would go their separate ways until the summer holidays were over. Then, with Edward going up to New College, and Vera herself a Somerville Exhibitioner (an education wrested from her reluctant middle-class parents who considered Oxford no place for a young lady) the autumn of 1914 promised much. Till then there was the summer to get through, and dreams of Roland in 'a scholar's gown swinging up St Giles's on [his] way to Somerville' in some misty, autumnal future would help to make it pass.

Only later when the pace of terrible events which overtook that summer had reduced such dreams to dust, abruptly foreshortening Vera's youth; when Roland had died of wounds in France, and Edward had been killed in action on the Italian Front; when Victor, blinded, had suffered a massive stroke, and Vera herself endured the fear and cold and butchery of a hospital camp near the Western Front, only then did she look back on this summer weekend as a last irreplaceable idyll before the Fall.

It became for her a moment when time stood still, after which things were never as happy, or as carefree, or as golden again. It came to stand for a vanished world, a time and place and innocence lost and never to be regained, and as such this fairly ordinary July weekend had to acquire a perfection of its own. To the survivors of the Great War the myth of the last golden summer was irresistible and they passed it on, surprisingly intact.

Indeed, a certain tradition has emerged in English literature and English history which sees the year 1914 as marking the sudden and decisive end of a golden age. It was a short idyll, according to the legend which has grown up around it, 'a brief little world'. 'Always the same picture,' it recalls 'home-made cakes and croquet, bright ideas, bright uniforms . . . high summer, the long days in the sun, slim volumes of verse, crisp linen, the smell of starch . . . ' 'What a romantic picture,' muses Jimmy Porter in John Osborne's 1950's play *Look Back in Anger*. 'The old Edwardian brigade do make their brief little world look pretty tempting.'

In *Take a Girl Like You* Osborne's contemporary Kingsley Amis has one of his characters imagine the type of man to suit his 1950's heroine. He would have died 'in 1914 or thereabouts', and would have proved a prince among suitors, an Edwardian paragon with the 'manners and the respect and the honour and the bunches of flowers and the attraction' of a man of his time. Only such a creature could emerge from the sunny, tranquil Eden which was his background – which was, indeed, England before the cruel betrayal and disillusionment of the First World War.

The myth of the golden age and of the last golden summer contains all the elements familiar to us from the myth of Eden. In it a sense of timelessness, a feeling of certainty, a sunlit pastoralism are held fast by the sticky bonds of nostalgia. The appeal of this time and place for us is heightened by the haunting realisation that, search as we will, all this is lost and will never be ours again. The summer of 1914 has become a lost Eden.

Indeed, so indelible is this idea that it has served as a prototype for other 'lost Edens' since. A nostalgic celebration by David Lowe of his generation, 'the last . . . of the Old South', recalls 'one spring in the early fifties . . . our summer of 1914 . . . Like those other generations who were given to witness the guillotining of a world, we never expected it. And like that of our counterparts, our world seemed most beautiful just before it disappeared.'

To those looking back at June and July 1914, chastened by the brutal knowledge of what came afterwards, the sky seemed bluer, the parties gayer – 'that last gay summer of a dying age' Duff Cooper called it – the girls sweeter and more girlish. A Londoner who pressed against Buckingham Palace railings the day before war broke out, on August 3, part of a huge, excited crowd waiting to catch a patriotic glimpse of the King, remembers in retrospect the geraniums in the flower-beds, redder than they had ever seemed to him before. Even Harold Macmillan, clear-sighted enough to acknowledge his 'somewhat rose-tinted spectacles', remembers *la douceur de vivre* . . . the lost sense of peace and security' that is the private preserve of those who knew England before the First World War.

But, 'It'll never come again,' says George Bowling in Orwell's *Coming Up For Air*, written in the 1930's, ' . . . the feeling inside you, the feeling of not being in a hurry, and not being frightened, the feeling you've either had and don't need to be told about, or haven't had and won't ever have the chance to learn.' 'It was the first time I heard a note of haste in anyone's voice,' a 1914 youth remembers of the day war broke out, August 4. 'My father was Master of the Rolls. We lived in Hyde Park Gate and I was having my tonsils out at home.

As I came out of the anaesthetic, I heard a newsboy along the Bayswater Road shouting, "War! War!" It seemed curious not so much for what he was saying as for the urgency in his voice. Haste – that is the difference between the world then and now.' 'Those who were born into the war,' wrote ex-combatant Richard Aldington looking back on what he remembered as a halcyon pre-war existence, 'can hardly understand the feeling of tranquil security which existed, the almost smug optimism of our lives.'

For those who had sufficient money, the period up to the First World War was undoubtedly one of ease, security and comfort. Britain was the richest country in the world and her wealth was the exclusive preserve of the upper and middle classes – no more and probably much less than a quarter of the population. Ninety-nine per cent of the land was not only in private hands but formed large estates, most of which had been in the same family for at least two generations. The landed elite, old aristocratic families like the Cecils, Russells, Howards and Bentincks, may have been losing their historic grip on the reins of power but they still retained fabulous wealth. At a time when there were adult men in full-time employment earning less than 25/– a week, the Duke of Rutland's revenue from rents alone came to well over £90,000. At Belvoir Castle, his massive 19th century gothic seat, the dining-room could seat eighty, and there was a private fire-brigade. The Duke of Portland's home, Welbeck Abbey, was so enormous that an underground railway was built to transport food quickly from the kitchens to those who were going to eat it. The Duke had several tennis courts in his grounds, positioned in different locations, so that he could play at all times of the day away from the direct glare of sunlight.

Lady Cynthia Asquith, herself the daughter of an earl and brought up on a Gloucestershire estate, came to the conclusion from watching her mother, that a large and hospitable country house was, despite its sizeable staff, a time-consuming burden to run. Domestic politics often turned out to be 'inflamed and preoccupying', as up to forty servants (Belvoir with fifty was an exception, 'absurd . . . a pantomime scene' as a 1914 visitor called it) jostled for rank and privilege. If the butler had his pantry with bedroom adjoining, the housekeeper's position demanded a parlour with a room to entertain the upper female servants. These, the ladies' maids such as Cynthia Asquith's who mended, darned and washed her wardrobe, needed a separate sitting room with tables for starching and sewing. In a sufficiently grand establishment the valets could boast a shoe room and brushing room, and all of these upper servants would expect their own bedrooms. The lower orders, by contrast, ate at a long table in the servants' hall, slept in attics and dormitories, and kept their clothes in lockers. Exactly matching accommodation had to be found for the servants of visitors who came to stay. At the Earl of Derby's house, where the King and Queen went for the Grand National in 1914, one hundred and twenty below-stairs staff looked after forty guests.

Doyenne of the female servants was the housekeeper, an imposing figure, white-capped and dressed in black, wielding keys, the symbol of her authority. Her domain was the rooms they unlocked: the china closet, the stillroom, the storeroom and linen cupboard. Under her and the ladies' maids came, in strict order of precedence, the parlour maids and housemaids, often country girls recommended by their vicar. While the parlour maid set tables, straightened covers, dusted ornaments and drew back the drawing-room curtains, her underling performed the hard physical labour which was the only path to promotion. Rising at five or six, the housemaids had the downstairs rooms cleaned, dusted and polished before the family in residence even came down to breakfast. They had swept the carpets (scattering damp tea leaves to lay the dust), blackleaded and polished the fireplace grates. They then sped upstairs while their employers ate – to make beds, tidy rooms, fling open windows and surreptitiously empty the chamber-pots, creeping with them down the back staircase so as not to offend the very people who had used them during the night. Plumbing even in 1914 was still a semi-luxury and scarce. A house with thirty bedrooms might boast only two lavatories and those jammed into pokey, inaccessible cupboards. One or two former bedrooms, meanwhile, had probably been converted into bathrooms by placing in them a giant, cast-iron, porcelain-enamelled tub. Nevertheless, some gentlemen were reluctant still to relinquish their hip-bath, taken in the privacy of their bedrooms in front of a warming fire, which necessitated the housemaids fetching can after can of boiling water.

After a hurried breakfast, interrupted by the tramp of parlour maids with heavy breakfast trays upstairs, the housemaids resumed their regime of scrubbing. Custom dictated that their work should be finished by midday, even when it was a morning for the carpets to be rolled up and beaten out of doors, while the floors they concealed were polished with beeswax or scrubbed white with soap, water and potassium carbonate. Downstairs the scullery maid carried in water for the distracted cook who had mouths to feed upstairs, downstairs and sometimes also in the schoolroom and nursery. It was the scullery maid's herculean task daily to blacklead the kitchen range, either with liquid Brunswick and Berlin Black or her own paste mixed from a lead block and water. When it was dry the range was polished till it gleamed. The newer bright steel ranges were expected to shine like a mirror too, with dousings of sweet-oil, rubbed fiercely with a leather. Small wonder that amongst maids such as these, on call to their employers (apart from one afternoon a week) fourteen or sixteen hours a day, those who could were deserting steadily to become factory-workers or to wait tables in the popular new tea-shops.

What did they do, these upper class Englishwomen who had everything done for them? They were not idle: on the contrary, they had devised for themselves a dizzy and often exhausting schedule of enjoyment to fill their time. The demands of fashion and of the social round were taxing. In April each year Society families shut down their country mansions and opened their town-houses in Mayfair or Belgravia. For three months until the end of July they gave themselves up to a single-minded pursuit of pleasure, entertaining each other at balls, operas, dinners, receptions, until Cowes Week brought the Season to a close at the end of July. In their narrow London houses so much space was demanded by the all-important reception rooms, that the family bedrooms often huddled cramped and close together on the upper floors. The children were banished even further afield – to the precarious isolation of the attics, where they continued their daily drudgery of lessons with the governess. The male servants, brought up from the country, and resplendent still – the footmen at least – in their London uniform of silk stockings, powdered wigs and breeches, slept over the stables, now used to house the motor-cars at the back of the houses.

The object of all this frantic socialising was the perpetuation of a caste. London, despite the estates in the country which provided their wealth, was still a magnet for these families, a show-case for their marriageable daughters, a proving-ground for their sons. Sir Philip Burne-Jones in 1914 bemoaned the fact that London Society was no longer small, exclusive and enclosed as it had been in the days when society hostesses set the fashion of not performing introductions at parties. Now a sea of unknown faces invariably greeted the old society hand as he entered each ballroom.

Nevertheless, in these London drawing-rooms, a younger girl might be expected to carry off a sufficiently rich and respectable husband. Debutantes in the first rank, as Lady Diana Manners, daughter of the Duke of Rutland, undoubtedly was when she came out in 1910, were expected to carry off rather more, a marchioness's or countess's coronet and a spread of thousands of acres at the least. Parental opposition was stiff when the beautiful Diana consorted with (and later married) Duff Cooper, a landless Foreign Office underling. But for the rest of the debutantes, years of quiet good breeding still counted for more than a dozen new ballgowns bought with brand-new money. There were often girls like Pearl Barrington Crake in 1914, whose army officer father was dead and who did the Season on comparatively little money, but who was invited every-where despite not being able to afford a party of her own, simply because she knew everyone.

At eighteen, her hopes as high as the hair piled for the first time on top of her head, the new debutante walked straight from the schoolroom into the drawing-room. In a white or pastel dress devoid of jewellery, she would come out overnight, usually at a large family dinner party, followed by a ball. She was not expected to be opinionated or vulgarly over-educated, but to listen interestedly, and to look as innocent as she undoubtedly was.

In these fashionable circles young wives, still childless, while they could don jewellery and bright colours and leave the strain of appearing virginal behind them, were still expected to behave with strict propriety. It was older married women who were, as the memoirs of the time seem to have it, 'fair game'. Sophisticated hostesses like Lady Desborough gathered a group of admiring young men, a 'culte' around them. They pushed their favourites even while the conventions of parenthood from a distance de-manded that they neglect their sons. The young men not unnaturally responded with sexual attentions and with extravagant and adulatory professions of gratitude and adoration. Part of it was the exaggerated and empty rhetoric of the time, but no doubt they were also grateful for the only opportunities they had of intimacy, or even privacy, with women of their own class.

This mutually satisfying game of courtship between older mar-ried women and their lovers was peculiar only to the highest circles, those still following the example set by Edward VII. Outside London morals and manners were significantly more straitlaced. In all the provincial striving to ape the far-off glamour of London society, a rigid code had developed which it became a crime to disregard. In Buxton in Derbyshire Vera Brittain was both mocked and pitied for her desire to leave home and attend a university. More normal was the fifteen-year-old girl in a London suburban household who had her own At Home cards printed in copperplate like her mother's.

It had been the advent of motorized transport which gave rise to the sprawling suburban growth of the early twentieth century. Linked to his place of work by railway, by underground, by electric tram and to London by a brand new fleet of motor-omnibuses, the suburban householder could afford to try for the best of both worlds. The solicitors, surgeons and successful businessmen who colonised the leafier hill-tops with their own large, detached villas were prosperous, conservative, solidly High Church and unhesitatingly Tory. In the richer suburbs their houses had spreading lawns, extensive well-stocked flower gardens, a kitchen garden and some- times an orchard and a tennis court as well. For suburban man the whole green and wooded acreage approximated to a passable imita- tion of country life.

Surrounded by neighbours in similar houses and circumstances to their own, most suburban families led agreeable, placid, if somewhat segregated and insular lives. Back in the security of the suburbs after his daily foray to the city, the commuter husband could read with a sense of comfortable detachment about such crises as the threat of war looming in the summer of 1914 in Ireland. His wife, whose sole function it was to be seen to be rich and therefore idle, arranged flowers, ordered food from her cook, and visited other wives much like herself in the neighbourhood. Her liberation from a life of routine domestic chores was achieved by a staff of maids and gardeners, nannies and nursemaids, sometimes even a groom turned chauffeur. As she retained still, despite the suffragettes, the Victorian sense of what was 'ladylike', it was the only liberation she envisaged or wanted. Indeed, if these suburban wives followed the suffragette movement in the newspapers at all, it was with amused and horrified incredulity. And if their sons went away to boarding- school, their daughters, even though they might have attended one of the new Girls' Public Day Schools, lived quietly at home as young women. Walks, tea at the tennis club, books chosen from the library, filled their sheltered, ordered days, until with luck they too could marry and set up house in emulation of their parents.

One step down from these prosperous households, the middle-middle classes inhabited streets of semi-detached houses with smaller gardens. But servants or at the very least a cook-general still ensured the family plenty of leisure time. They spent it conscientiously. Cricket, croquet, football, bowling clubs, amateur dramatics, musical societies, stamp-collecting, wireless telegraphy, gardening and photography – the network of suburban clubs and activities in 1914 was already extensive. For some families the nearness of the country – rural lanes still ran behind many suburban gardens, a haven for animals and wild flowers – was an invitation to venture further afield. Every Sunday up to 1914 club groups or families of cyclists filled the roads out of town to the country or the sea. On Reigate Hill, a famous gathering-point, the grassy banks were lined with bicycles, summer flowers tied to their handlebars. Those who stayed at home in the hot summer weather longed for the water-cart to appear to level the dust on their untarmac-ed roads. They might have been less welcoming to the organ-grinder, the lavender-woman, the geranium-seller, the gypsies selling birch brooms at every back door, and the tinkers who haunted suburban roads offering to mend buckets or grind knives.

The daughters of middle-class suburban households did not come out, but in the true country gently-born girls of the upper middle classes made their debut in local county society. They mixed with the children of army officers, vicars or squires, at dinners or at the few local balls. In 1914 Violet Graham, a nineteen-year-old, was languishing in a minor country house in North Wales. 'I was supposed to be out but there was nothing much to do. I'd only been to three dances, one of which was for the local hospital.' Such families did not go often to London. They bought their clothes ready-made in a store in the nearest provincial town. Or, if she could be trusted, the local dressmaker sewed her clothes. Their entertainments, tennis, otter-hunting, card evenings and local fêtes, were equally home-made. Their leisure time was guaranteed by a household of servants. The parlour maid waited at table; the housemaid lit fires and dusted the bedrooms; the cook prepared four-course dinners each night; the head groom had been kept on to drive the new car. 'There was no butler or footman,' Edith Reid, a stockbroker's daughter commented, 'but *we* certainly didn't have to do anything. If Papa was doing well on the Stock Exchange, we could afford a between-maid for the cook.'

The golden summer of the few in 1914 was guaranteed by the servitude of the many. Almost half a million men and women were employed in domestic service. For the middle or upper-class mistress, Ireland had long been a source of cheap, pliable domestic labour. Bessie Ellis, twenty-seven in the summer of 1914, came over from County Longford in 1910 when she was twenty-three. 'It was all very poor small farms there. My father was a small farmer but my mother and father both died. Relations came and put down a day's pay for what they had done, and they hadn't done anything. We never made much of it.' Among her contemporaries, 'lots of young women, no end of them, went into service. It was either that or the workhouse. I used to scrub floors. I got less than 1/- a day – terrible wages – but I lived in and got food.' Then rescue came. 'I knew a lady in Ireland and she recommended me to some English friends of hers.'

The English friend was a country vicar whose parish was Brenchley, a small village in Kent. Alone and carrying her few belongings, Bessie made the long journey by boat and train, finally arriving at Paddock Wood, Brenchley's nearest station. 'No-one was there when I turned up. By luck I saw an old shunter. I told him and he said, "You can walk up to Brenchley with me." Even when I arrived at the vicarage, I couldn't find the way in. It had two entrances and I went round and round, till at last I met someone who helped me, a housemaid called Kent. The first night she took me to a concert at the schoolhouse, meaning to be kind, I suppose. But I slept through it. I'd been travelling all night and I'd had nothing at all to eat.

'At twelve when I went in to service, Mother set me up with my uniform. It had to last. I wore a black dress, white apron and a white cap with streamers. The white aprons got black almost as soon as you put them on. Each morning, first thing, I had to clean the kitchen range – smother it with black lead and rub like the devil. My, it used to shine. Then there was a brass fender in front and a huge dresser with plates on and brass utensils which were never used. They got dirty just by sticking there but I had to clean them just the same. I had to try and work the kitchen fire to keep it going all night. One evening I put wood on and heard a roaring in the middle of the night. The water was boiling, and the lady of the house was down putting the fire out.'

Bessie began her employment in Brenchley as the kitchen maid. 'I learnt as I went along. I worked my way up through the washing-up, peeling the vegetables, preparing the cooking-pots. It took me till 1914 before I was allowed to do anything important.' But even then additional responsibilities did not reduce her workload. 'There weren't enough of us servants and it was a large family. When I knelt to pray those first nights [in the attic bedroom she shared with Kent], I often went to sleep on my knees. But I was all right in the end. I picked things up very quickly.'

To Hilda French, a sixteen-year-old maid-of-all-work drudging in a middle-class home in the London suburb of Kingston, the possibility of life outside domestic service seemed in 1914 unthinkable, an unimaginable dream.

'I left school at fourteen. There was nothing but service. We were working-class but not poor working-class. Father saw that we done everything right. In those days over table manners and stuff children had to mind their parents. We got a clout for giggling at table.

'There were four rooms and four of us – two boys and me and my younger sister. It was all right when we could still sleep together. After that I had to go. For the very poor there was jam factories or bottling beer sometimes. If you were a little more middle-class than us there was dressmaking, or girls had just started to go into shops. I wanted to go dressmaking, but they wanted the room. My brother who was older than me went downstairs. My younger brother and sister were left.

'The 2nd January 1912 was my fourteenth birthday. I thought I would have a fortnight's holiday but after Christmas I was out. I started in service on the Monday for five shillings a week. I was totally independent. I never went back to them for anything again. Mother did set me up, buying two of everything. It meant a lot in those days – two chemises, two knickers, two petticoats. Your mum always set you up in your first place.

'It was a house in Kingston, my first place, a Mrs Rowbotham. I wore a blue cotton frock and a white apron.

[21]

The first day she said to me, "I want you to clean the grates."
You wore a coarse apron when you cleaned the grates and it
was as black as the grate when you'd finished. There were
four of them. My ma had told me to do it properly, so what I
done, I took all day. I was very glad to get to bed. I was so
miserable, I cried silently. The woman said, "That's very
nice, Hilda, but you'll have to do it quicker."

'I wanted to be a children's nurse and the only chance
was in big service. I went to a big house and stuck it in the
nursery for a month. I started work at six-thirty and I was
head-cook and bottle-washer. I had to clean the prams and
make the nursery meals though that was the tweenie's job. I
said to the cook one night when it was 9.30 and I was handed
the darning, "When do you get time to yourself?" She said,
"When you're in bed." I daren't go home and tell my pa.
You were all so scared. You always had to look after your
character. "You'll lose your character," was what they said.

'I nearly lost mine anyway. I was young and a bit
attractive. The boot boy put a note in my boots and the old
cook found it. It said: "Dear Hilda, I love you. Will you meet
me on your day off?" I was summoned to the drawing-room
and the Master told me off in front of his four or five
children, and that I wasn't to flirt. I went home crying. My
dad said, "Leave." I couldn't go back home though. I didn't
go back home for anything. My sister had been turned out
now too. My brother was in the motoring trade – Zenith
motor-bikes. My dad put us all into something. But they
couldn't afford to keep us. Anyway, the idea of going into
service was to train to be a good housewife. Jam factories
were the lowest. Service was right for the proper working-
class.'

Within the working-class there was a marked variation in lifestyle
and income. While all worked hard, there were those who returned
after a twelve or fourteen-hour day at the coal-face, in the mills or in
the factories, to living conditions of the meanest, drabbest, filthiest
kind. Darkness, squalor, overcrowding, under-nourishment, produced children with rickets, adults stunted in growth or with the
pallor of anaemia. Soup kitchens, literacy drives and temperance
schemes were the palliatives prescribed by the more charitable

among the upper and middle-class. But it rarely occurred to them that their enjoyment of such articles as hair brushes, silk flowers, leather-bound books, fur collars, even corsets, was dependent on whole families toiling at piece work from dawn till dusk in the miserable sweatshop trade. 'The poor were just there, we didn't think about them,' says one upper-middle-class young girl. Lady Violet Brandon in Paul Thompson's book *The Edwardians* is quoted as recalling 'these terrible things you thought were just lumps of rags . . . and then . . . there was a tramp . . . "Tramp" was a word that filled one with horror.' Such an attitude was probably fairly typical.

Mark Hayler, a young man from South Norwood, a respectable South London suburb, looked on the poverty-stricken masses with the campaigning zeal typical of the free-thinking, nonconformist lower middle classes. Deeply religious and a forceful member for all his twenty-seven years, of the temperance group, United Kingdom Alliance, he spent much of the summer of 1914 listening to evidence in court. What preoccupied him was a court case brought by UK Alliance against the manufacturers of the tonic *Wincarnis*, alleged to contain wine and yet marketed as pure 'beef extract' rather than the more general 'extract of beef'.

Hayler came from the North of England. His childhood influences were liberal and nonconformist. 'My grandfather was a Chartist. We had always belonged to all the movements. It was the sort of independent background and thinking that turned me into a pacifist and a Quaker.' From 1905 till 1909 he had worked in the estate office of Naworth Castle in Cumberland. 'Then one day the Master [Lord Carlisle] said, "I want you in London for the season." I went down with the horses and carriages, like one of the chattels. They had a house in Kensington, in Palace Green. It still had horses and carriages in the stables behind it. They went to dances in them. It was a Victorian set-up entirely. The Earl and Countess were at daggers drawn though. They sent notes to each other and he did everything to annoy her – like opening parcels in a corner of the room so that she couldn't see. Her ladyship was insatiably curious. Her son, Geoffrey Howard MP, was Private Secretary to Mr Asquith. Every night when he came back from the House the Countess waited up for him, and called him into the drawing-room to give a full report. She was very bossy. The 'radical countess', they called her. John Morley said if she had been a man, she would have been Prime Minister. Lady Carlisle was very kind to me, mind. She had thirteen children. One of them, Lady Mary, married the Greek scholar, Gilbert Murray. He said, knowing I was a Quaker, if he had ever wanted to belong to a religious group, it would have been the Society of Friends. Lord Carlisle was the oldest trustee of the National Gallery. Holman Hunt came once to see the pictures and Lord Carlisle turned to me and asked casually, "Will you take him round?" It was quite a thrill. I asked him about *The Light of the World*. He said he had a lamp made specially in Palestine for it.'

Since January of 1914 Mark Hayler, now a committed southerner, had put his estate training to use in a job for the English Forestry Association.

'I worked for the Secretary there, a man called, believe it or not, Mr du Chêne. I used a dictaphone (made by His Master's Voice) to transcribe and type the letters the Secretary dictated on to cylinders at home. The EFA had no money or means. It was practically voluntary. It planted trees and grew the wood for country people to make tools and handicrafts. It was a trying place, always on the brink, and Mr du Chêne was ill and difficult to work with. Fortunately, I had other interests when I left in the spring of 1914.

'I had two jobs offered me then. One was from a solicitor, whom I didn't like, in Bognor Regis. When it came to the other, which I wanted, I made a bit of a mess of the interview. It was at Warrington, near Manchester, one of the early Reformatory Schools. I told Mr Jones, the Governor, that I was rather a freelance and hadn't been used to nine to five. He was a bit taken aback. 'He said, "I've got another man in view. If *he* doesn't come, would you consider it?" I went away knowing I'd said the wrong thing and that I'd made a mistake. I was out of work for a long time after that – all through the summer. I only had one job more before the Conscription Act – and prison.'

The Haylers' mode of life, their interests, their moral standards, were, according to J. B. Priestley (who lived in 1914 in much the same circumstances in Bradford, Yorkshire) typical of the cultural environment of the lower-middle-class English suburb. These were, he claimed, 'shop and chapel' people, terrified of sinking back into the working-classes they had sprung from, clinging to a hard-won respectability which made them on occasion narrow-minded

and cautious. Housed in the dreariest of the terraced streets which –
the legacy of a 1910–1913 building boom – marched in red-roofed
rows far out from the city centres, they were the backbone of the
Liberal Party, the mainstay of nonconformist religion. Despite their
relative poverty, this section of the population, as J. B. Priestley has
pointed out, contributed greatly to cultural life. These people –
ordinary teachers, office-workers, small businessmen and shop-
keepers – abhorred hire-purchase and could not afford luxury. But
once they had saved for special events such as their holiday (taken
annually perhaps in August in a seaside boarding-house), they had
money to spare for books and music and other activities they deemed
important. Mark Hayler continually bought books, subscribed to
magazines and went to watch the Hallé Orchestra and the London
Symphony. Family tastes and entertainments were simple. 'We had
a nice garden. We played croquet. We made baskets, sewed, did
handicrafts. We were all good with our hands. My father would take
my mother out for drives in a hired landau, to places like West
Wickham, sitting on the box. My mother sat sedately inside the
carriage. Sitting on a box was man's business. It was all country then
out there and wooded. I saw my first two aeroplanes there in 1914.
One looped the loop.'

Like J. B. Priestley's mother, Mark Hayler's mother did all the
cooking, buying fruit and vegetables from carts that come up the
street and delivered to the door. She had a 'char' to help her keep
the front room neat and clean for visitors, but she herself seldom left
the house. 'I remember meeting her once in the street,' says Mark
Hayler, 'and taking her somewhere. That was the only time I ever
went out anywhere alone with my mother.' Instead, with eight
children living at home, she devoted herself to their welfare. 'My
mother's idea was to make home so comfortable that none of us
would marry. She would say, "What do you want to leave home for,
aren't you happy here?" So there we were at home – my four sisters,
all music teachers, and my three brothers, one of them ten years
older than me. We were a very happy family. When it came to war –
and prison – no family could have supported me more.'

'Unless we tear ourselves away,' wrote J. B. Priestley of the last
Edwardian summer, 'from garden-parties, balls, Ascot, extravagant
weekends, and remember these rebels from the middle classes,
meeting in little groups all over the country, lighting up some of the
dreariest towns . . . by an evening's enthusiasm, we do not under-

stand the . . . age. The atmosphere of hopeful debate, the liberating eagerness, the spirit of good-humoured rebellion did not survive the war.' His father and his friends like Mark Hayler were socialists, but it was 'rather a naive socialism . . . a kind of utopian dream', which after the war faded away. 'Too many terrible things had happened. Part of the hopefulness vanished too . . . the rather innocent hopefulness of the era.'

2

May

ALREADY IN EARLY MAY it promised to be a fine summer. The cream of Society, flocking back like migratory birds for the Season, were surprised to find England in May as warm and sunny as the South of France they had recently left behind. At Hawthorn Hill, where the Household Brigade Steeplechases brought them together for one of the first engagements in the 1914 Season, there was no need for the glowing coal-braziers which customarily warmed the race-going crowd.

The spectacle in the bright May sunshine was dazzling; the clothes – rainbow-striped, black and white checked – dramatic, if not as feminine as the pastel curves of the Edwardian era. Indeed, lamented the staid and stuffy *Tatler*, 'One sighs . . . for the simpler outlines of last year . . . [Skirts] short and skimpy but very loudly checked or striped . . . hats rather rakish than becoming, whose trimmings straggle wildly skywards, and everywhere except round the feet a general superfluity of drapes – these are the features of the mode of the moment.' Quite 'the thing' then was Lady Diana Manners ('charming and ubiquitous', the *Tatler* noted, and even in this the first week of the Season), in her straight checked skirt, draped overtunic and checked hat with its two sweeping feathers. Nellie Hozier, Winston Churchill's sister-in-law, dressed more sedately but wearing one of the lace-collars that were newly fashionable, stayed close to Monica Grenfell, who could revel in her acquaintance with Gustav Hamel, one of the stars of the occasion. Indeed, during the many afternoons he had spent looping the loop at Taplow, Monica, along with half of Society, had fallen in love with the daredevil young Swedish airman who stylishly embodied the new fashionable craze for flying. 'I have become the *Flying Machine Bore* for life,' shrugged Etty Desborough. Diana Manners, never allowed in Hamel's 'mothy aeroplane', sighed with envy at Sybil

Hart-Davis who, held precariously by two shoulder-straps in a machine otherwise open to the elements, became one of the first women ever to loop the loop. (Later, so the story went, Hamel took her up once more clutching two squealing piglets, to prove to his friends that pigs could fly.)

Returning to London, the race-goers found the city en fête with flowers and bustling with visitors. Since March the familiar rows of small green chairs had stood out in Hyde Park, an invitation for passers-by to sit down in the warm spring sunshine and admire the tulips, daffodils and hyacinths bordering the newly-raked gravel paths. In Mayfair and Belgravia the shutters were drawn back from the great white houses. Window-boxes and striped awnings made the streets blaze with colour. With the return of the King and Queen from Paris on April 24th, the hotels were filling up: the Season of 1914 was under way.

On May 1st the first large ball took place in a Lowndes Square mansion. In the side-garden a vast marquee had been erected, its ceiling painted dark blue to imitate the night sky. A black-and-white chequered dance floor had been laid across the lawns and flower-beds, in its centre a miniature lake on which floated water-lilies lit by coloured lights. Around the sides a colonnade of white columns and banks of flowering hawthorns provided a backdrop for those of the eight hundred guests who wished to sit out the dancing. They included the Prime Minister, most of the Diplomatic Corps and Cabinet and, mingling with Society, the leading figures of the London stage. Osbert Sitwell, a twenty-one-year-old officer stationed fortuitously in Wellington Barracks throughout the summer season, sampled the social world and found it, 'more miscellaneously composed than ever it had been . . . [There was] a sweet and carefree atmosphere . . . Never had Europe been so prosperous and gay.' Along with his young contemporaries, 'The belles of the Edwardian summer survived in a kind September splendour,' and danced with young men fifty or sixty years their junior until 4 a.m.

Lady Mond, giver of the May Day ball and married to a Liberal peer, was an American by birth. 'The American hostess,' sniffed the *Tatler*, 'generally gets there of course . . . by virtue of her command of tons and tons of filthy lucre.' The 'American peeress', Lady Cheylesmore, was publicly castigated for her *nouveau riche* extravagance with flowers – roses in the supper-room at her dance, lilies-of-the-valley on the tables, sweet peas and poppies in the

ballroom, roses rambling up the stairs. Society professed indignation, too, at the expensive American 'favours' chosen for each guest,
although none of those opening their gold cigarette-cases and
jewellery in Lady Cheylesmore's supper-room seemed indignant
enough to refuse them.

Lady Mond and, in Belgrave Square, fresh-faced homely Countess Beauchamp for the Liberal Party; the slender, pretty Duchess of
Portland for the cause of Unionism – the efforts made by London's
political hostesses were indefatigable and incessant. In Park Lane, in
a great square house recently painted white, the strong-willed,
energetic Marchioness of Londonderry entertained for the Conservative Party. Her rival, Lady Lansdowne, at home in a Georgian
house in Berkeley Square, had a calendar for once more social than
political, 1914 being a year of her granddaughter's coming-out.

In fashionable magazines, those who had prepared for a rigorous
Season during April in Cannes read how they could recuperate from
it in Baden-Baden or St Moritz in early autumn. But just now there
were suitcases to be unpacked, last-minute visits to the dressmaker
to be arranged and drawing-rooms to be aired all over Mayfair and
Belgravia. In the gold and rose-brocade drawing-room of Ches-
terfield House, the American Duchess of Roxburghe resumed her
select candlelit soirées, so much more intimate than the grand
receptions held under dazzling rock crystal and ormulu chandeliers.
In Carlton House Terrace, the American Mrs Mackay arranged
more musical evenings in her Georgian house transformed inside
into an Italian palazzo, with French furniture covered in Gobelin
tapestry and a white marble staircase said by *Vanity Fair* to have cost
sixty thousand pounds.

The Americans, noted *Vanity Fair* in its last May issue, were
everywhere this Season. American hostesses, like Lady Cunard,
invariably held the biggest, smartest dinner-parties. Even Crewe
House had been let to an American, the admittedly charming Mrs
Duke. But 'So many houses are changing hands now,' the writer
complained, 'I hear the Queen is far from pleased at the way . . .
some of the bigger hostesses are absenting themselves from town
. . .' Headquarters of the 'American set' was Mrs John Astor's Adam
house in Grosvenor Square, a few doors down from the Italian
Embassy where rows of red-and-gold liveried servants traditionally
lined up to greet the guests like footguards on parade. At the other
extreme, the modern Lady Drogheda who had set a trend by taking

up falconry on the golf-course at Cannes, displayed to Society a drawing-room completely redesigned in Futurist black, the brain-child of a leading contemporary artist.

If Lady Drogheda stood for the avant-garde, Osbert Sitwell's aunt Lady Londesbrough was irretrievably Edwardian, (although her husband's passion was modern music: Ravel, Stravinsky, Schönberg and other composers, of whom his guests, 'busy toeing the monotonous gilded line . . . from Ascot to Goodwood to Cowes' would not have heard). In her marble-walled house in Green Street, Lady Londesbrough gave stylish parties, at which Bimbi, a pink-turbaned youth brought home from India, stood 'directing the guests in the manner of an 18th century page'. Bimbi was one Indian souvenir in constant use. The Londesbroughs' country home, how-ever, according to their nephew, was lined with 'large presentation portraits of jewelled and dusky potentates which, in spite of their colour, resembled white elephants in size and usefulness'. Alongside Bimbi, another Green Street fixture was Osbert's cousin, the Duchess of Beaufort, whose two horsey daughters longed visibly for the summer to be over and the autumn hunting-season at home in Badminton to arrive.

Among the London hostesses, Osbert Sitwell's two especial favourites were Mrs Keppel, Edward VII's former mistress, and the elderly Lady Brougham. He admired them in the first instance for their taste. Lady Brougham, a sprightly Victorian figure in black silk with a white lace cap, drove round 1914 London still in the brougham named after her husband's family. Brought up in Flor-ence, she herself was the daughter of a famous connoisseur, and one of the few in the fussy Victorian era to retain a Georgian simplicity in her Chesham Place home. 'Everything [there],' recalled Osbert Sitwell admiringly, 'formed part of an engrossing work of art . . . [It was] full of character, even down to the huge 18th century volume of coloured engravings of flowers which stood propped open on an 18th century chair, on the landing at the top of the stairs, as if to refresh you after the climb. These plates showed . . . exotic blos-soms, and nearly every day were . . . opened at a different place.' As to real flowers, Lady Brougham contrived arrangements 'never . . . seen in other houses, huge arching sprays of green *cymbidium* with scarlet centres, or the coralline shields of the anthurium'. Her exquisite furniture included some rare Italian pieces, for example a 17th century tortoiseshell cabinet, which she had been known to offer carelessly to guests who seriously admired it. Despite these surroundings, Lord and Lady Brougham remained in appearance strict Victorians. Already seventy-eight in 1914 (he would live until 1927 when he was ninety-one), Lord Brougham was one of the last men in London to wear the Victorian striped shirt and stiff collar tailored all in one piece.

Mrs Keppel, too, owned a Georgian house but her vast, lavish Grosvenor Square mansion far outdid the cramped prettiness of Green Street. Osbert Sitwell luxuriated in its 'grey walls, red lacquer cabinets, English 18th century portraits of people in red coats, huge porcelain pagodas and thick, magnificent carpets'. There guests would find their tall, fair hostess invariably engrossed in her favourite game of bridge, while smoking cigarettes through a fashionable, elongated holder. Her husky-voiced, exotic daughter Violet was an acknowledged beauty, nicknamed by those who reported the 1914 Season, as one of 'The Three Graces'. Slim, pale Nancy Cunard and the exquisite, creamy-skinned Diana Manners were the other two.

Lady Cunard, Nancy's mother, was also a celebrated London hostess, perhaps the most striking and cosmopolitan among them. 'Lady Cunard,' recalled Harold Acton, 'delighted in mixing her guests like cocktails with unexpected ingredients. The gazelles were induced to sit beside the lions ... The shy stranger would be introduced in a brief expository phrase: "He has just flown in from Finland ... writing a biography of Sibelius ... "' Her unstinting admirer, Acton, likened Maud Cunard's arrival in her drawing-room, almost always late, to 'a burst of melody'. Lady Cunard's detractors, though, were equally vivid in the comparisons they made. Sir Harold Nicolson, compelled to sit through a 'ghastly dinner, supposed to be literary,' with George Moore, 'talk[ing] rubbish about all great writers having lovely names ... What a silly old man!' derided his hostess as 'looking like a third-dynasty mummy' which some amateur had painted pink.

The glamorous Lady Cunard was born in San Francisco as plain Maud Burke, of a family that was well off but not well bred. Her passport into Society was marriage to a middle-aged English baronet she met in New York. Sir Bache Cunard, whose grandfather founded the mighty shipping line, owned Nevill Holt, a vast edifice of towers and cloisters and crenellated walls deep in the English shires. Rich he may have been but his tastes were those of a country squire. In 1911 Lady Cunard, bored with country life, fled Nevill Holt and rented a house in Cavendish Square belonging to Herbert Asquith, the Prime Minister. The dining-table was lapis-lazuli, the curtains lamé in poison green. A huge painting of giraffes among silver birch trees covered one wall. Outside in the hall a Chinese incense-burner scented the air.

Lady Cunard's pretensions were scorned by many persons prominent in Society. The aristocratic Virginian Lady Astor resented being linked by nationhood with brash new immigrants to America's Far and Middle West. Harold Nicolson, who reported this, displayed the insularity and reactionary snobbishness of many Englishmen of his time, believing that 'every American is more or less as vulgar as any other American.' Nevertheless, Lady Cunard won the loyalty and intimate confidences of some English Society women, among them Diana Manners's mother the 'artistic duchess'. Violet Rutland cut a romantic figure whose costume, despite the changing fashions, seldom varied. To ivory or palest tea-coloured chiffon and lace, frothing at the neck and sleeves with ribbons, ruffles and jabot, she pinned during the day a sprig of bay leaves, her emblem. Her hats, to the despair of Lady Cunard who presented her with the latest Paris fashions, copied mediaeval coifs, Russian headdress or even the wimple of a nun.

To her daughter Diana and to Lady Cunard's daughter Nancy, these two were ironically 'Her Grace' and 'Her Ladyship'. All four spent the 1913 season in Venice together, where Lady Cunard had rented a *palazzo*. Here Nancy, a fascinated newcomer just out of the schoolroom, became embroiled in the glamorous escapades of Diana's circle, known as the 'Corrupt Coterie'. In particular, she helped Diana join Duff Cooper and his friends on the Adriatic shore for midnight bathing-parties, an adventure which when discovered reduced both mothers to a storm of tears.

Back home in London in spring 1914 Nancy prepared to be launched as one of that Season's debutantes. It was an unwilling debut on Nancy's part, mother and daughter arguing fiercely about the clothes suitable for such a venture. Lady Cunard favoured a girlish image for her daughter, with puffed sleeves and flower-trimmed hats. Like most mothers of her time she considered rose-tinted lip-salve and a dusting of powder more than adequate for a young girl's make-up. Nancy, for her part, determined on a wardrobe full of turbans and dashing berets. She hoarded a private cache of theatre make-up – greasepaint, white powder, and rouge which she applied to her cheeks with a hare's foot. By the end of a pre-season buying spree, shopping for ball-gowns at Monsieur Poiret's smart Parisian salon, and a visitation to Marthe Callot to acquire tea-gowns, afternoon dresses, Ascot costumes, 'bloozes' and skirts to wear at country weekends, Nancy was referring to her mother as a 'polished termagant'. Only over furs did they agree, and their joint biographer Daphne Fielding has painted a vivid picture of them standing 'side by side, leopard-clad, in front of the triple mirror at Bradleys, eyeing their similar reflections with approval'.

Lady Cunard did not approve of Nancy's choice of friends. In contrast to her usual casually eclectic guest-list she gave much thought in May 1914 to drawing up a list of suitable young men who would partner Nancy and her fellow-debutantes at the succession of small dances she planned. But with the example of the 'Corrupt Coterie' before her, Nancy made haste to establish her own set, who met most evenings at a Percy Street restaurant, the Eiffel Tower. The owner of this French-sounding establishment was a jovial Austrian, Rudolf Stulich. Long after the official closing-hours, his patrons continued to make merry in the room (decorated by Wyndham Lewis) upstairs, or drink champagne in the downstairs dining-room with its shaded table-lights and windows carefully shuttered. Stulich cashed cheques, took in the temporarily homeless and not surprisingly died a pauper. His favourite joke was to offer clients brandy from Augustus John's private bottle. Here, with cronies like Osbert Sitwell and Iris Tree, Nancy spent many evenings, 'drinks held long in one hand, while the other unwinds a discussion', in what Edward Marsh called 'her high little squeaky toneless voice'. 'If ever we go to heaven in a troop,' she wrote nostalgically later, 'the Tower must be our ladder / Vertically . . .'

Among Nancy Cunard's fellow-debutantes that summer were Sir Robert Peel's granddaughter Alexandrine von der Heydt and Clarissa Tennant, niece of the Prime Minister by marriage. Herbert Asquith's daughter Elizabeth was due to accompany her cousin to their first State Ball. The Duchess of Devonshire was bringing out the first of her five marriageable daughters and vying with Lady Curzon to give the most glittering party. It was said that Princess Mary herself would be a debutante the following winter.

But there were others doing the 1914 Season on a more modest scale. Pearl Barrington Crake was one. 'We weren't well off,' she remembers, 'but we were very happy. And I went to everything.' Her debut had been a dance held in late December 1913 at her uncle's Yorkshire home, for which the famous Casano came up all the way from London with his six-piece band. 'So I was out dancing in the last summer before the war. That was my time.' Like others who enjoyed that last summer of peace it seems somewhat frivolous to her now looking back on the winter which came afterwards. 'Rather flippant – going to masses of dances wherever I was. You just went off across England. I probably didn't come home for ten days during which I'd have been to three or four dances. And in those days you *really* danced.'

Home for Pearl's family, her sister and her widowed mother, was in Kensington's South Street near Thurloe Square. 'Number 29 ... That is where I lived from when I was ten and where I was married from and where all my children were born. After my father died we went there and there we stayed. That's why I went away for nearly every weekend if I was asked.'

As a young, shy debutante, the 1914 Season seemed 'the most gay summer I've ever known. One night I went to five dances in one night. The only year to rival it was the quite hectic summer of 1919 when people hadn't done anything for five years, so they all had dances.' For three brief summer months her life was a curious mix of grand social spectacle on a lavish scale, and homely evenings spent playing 'very ordinary' bridge and cool-can in Thurloe Square. Money, for a family in their social stratum, was scarce. 'We only went out,' she remembers, 'when we were taken to anything. Mother never bought a thing. The only things we did with her were concerts, a few cinemas and skating-rinks. We used to go to these wonderful Sunday concerts at the Albert Hall. Or make toffee – you burnt it generally – on wet July afternoons. Or you got up all your friends and roller-skated in Holland Park – that was the great place. Then we had tea or orange drinks or something. Luckily for us travelling was cheap then for we were never allowed to use taxis. They were very expensive, 6d or a shilling. We went by bus or we walked.'

A tall, graceful blonde, Pearl could, from her photographs, wear clothes well. It was fortunate as 'if you weren't well-off, which we weren't, you tried to get through each season on three dresses. The very well-off girls [like Nancy Cunard] would have six dresses at least.' Her clothes were bought at Debenhams or else, 'you vaguely designed your own. You went to a dance and you saw perfectly lovely dresses of girls all very much better off than yourself and you would remember a pretty sleeve or something and come home and say, "I think I'll go and get some stuff and we'll make a dress like that." The stuffs were lovely. All embroidered.' With her 'tiny dress allowance' she would then visit 'wonderful Miss Somebody – there were so many marvellous little dressmakers – in Walpole Street.' Together they would cut out a paper pattern and copy the idea. 'It was such fun and the dressmakers were terribly good at it.' For the daytime there were calf-length skirts and suits and blouses to be made. And hats to buy: 'Never, never, never did you go out without a hat. It was either a pull-on felt, perfectly plain, very smart, or a regular Basque beret in black, grey or brown which was what I wore at home.' Pearl's fair hair, piled high in a coil, took a long time to dress. 'I think we were much more careful about our hair in those days. You *brushed* your hair far more. Or your maid did.' It took Pearl's maid on average an hour and a half to prepare her for a dance. And yet she wore no make-up except a light dusting of powder. 'I remember,' she says, 'I went to India in 1922 and stayed at Vice-Regal lodge where Lady Hardwick said to me (because I was frightfully fair, white fair then), "Pearl, I think you ought to put some colour in your cheeks. I think you ought to put some lipstick on." I'd never put lipstick on and it was 1922. Certainly never back in 1914. But you see we were quite presentable without it.'

So Pearl, clutching her dressmaking patterns, travelled by bus backwards and forwards from Kensington to Walpole Street, while in Cavendish Square Nancy Cunard unpacked her *haute couture* Parisian dresses. Already by every post applications were arriving seeking admission in June to Ascot's hallowed Royal Enclosure. To Lord Churchill, the *Tatler* reported, fell the task of deciding who would or would not enter Society's portals. 'His task gets stiffer and stiffer' every year, the *Tatler* declared, as more and more tried to join 'that very elastic body'. Harvey Nichols sent out to their customers a brochure of new summer fashions: seven and a half guineas for an evening gown of pale pink taffeta belted in saxe-blue moiré, with sleeves of écru lace, roses on the shoulder and a diamanté buckle. For the middle classes there was the chance to spend May on the Bournemouth beaches, as the unseasonable heat prompted the railways to lay on cheap excursion fares especially early. For the upper classes though, there was no such escape. Daily *The Times* reported the arrival of august personages in the capital. For them the stage was set for a glittering and exhausting London Season.

The first week in May saw the traditional spectacle of the Naval and Military Tournament at Olympia, and the equally familiar sight of nannies comforting those of their young charges upset by all the 'bang-banging'. There was more 'bang-banging' at the Hendon Aviation Meeting where a bomb-dropping competition was amongst the entertainments planned. The Royal Aero Club had occasion to censure a member for flying too low and noisily over an automobile-race. Queen Alexandra attended Hendon, along with her sister, former Empress Marie of Russia. From the ground they watched the Kaiser's daughter take off in a Germany military airship.

It was to prove a busy month for the British Royal Family, ushered in by the funeral on May 8 of Princess Louise's husband, the old Duke of Argyll. Prince Henry of Prussia visited the King and Queen to offer his condolences and many in Society donned mourning-dress. (It was convenient, observed the *Tatler* wickedly, that black and navy were this year's colours.) The day before had found the King in Bloomsbury opening the British Museum's Edward VII Galleries named after his father, '[an] oasis in the wilderness of boarding-houses,' said one paper, 'and not far from the Georgian quarters of the quarrelling Cubists.' King George and Queen Mary's next engagement was in the second week of May, when the Danish Royal Family paid a state visit to Britain. Part of the burden of entertaining them would fall on Queen Alexandra who was the Danish King's aunt. Indeed, King Christian's first weekend in London was spent *en famille* at Marlborough House. King George ended off the month with five 'working days' spent in the company of his troops barracked at Aldershot. Relations between the Army and Their Majesties, boomed a leader in *The Times*, were as a result very much improved – 'in much closer touch and sympathy' than at the accession.

Meanwhile, the undergraduates of Oxford and Cambridge, the *Tatler* reported in May, had gone up for the summer term after a six-week vacation in 'glorious summer weather' – a contrast to 1908, when they returned to find snow, floods and leaking roofs. At Balliol Harold Macmillan, by now in his second year, had settled down to the 'curious mixture of comfort and hardship' that Oxford then offered.

'The first event of the day [ran an Edwardian guide] is of course attendance at the College Chapel . . . The propriety of commencing the day's work in the house of God is undeniable . . . Attendance at eight o'clock chapel insures early rising. A pleasant breakfast is the proper antecedent of a pleasant day. Then follows, if the man be wise, three hours of hard reading. The study is liable to be broken by lectures [which] will tempt him to call on some friend, or saunter down "The High". Such temptations must be resisted . . .

'Generally no one reads much beyond one, nor is it wise to attempt to pass that hour, and place too much strain upon the brain . . . The especial period for heavy luncheons is the Summer Term, in the presence of fair cousins or sisters. But the boating-man cannot allow himself a large luncheon, with two or three glasses of sherry . . .

'Boating as practised at Oxford is not an unmixed pleasure, and the necessity of sitting quietly in *deshabillé* beneath a steady rain tends naturally to diminish the enthusiasm of a novice . . . But though Oxford is primarily and properly an intellectual resort, it is no secret that the position of a College upon the river and in the cricket-field is the index to its popularity . . . For one of a College eleven there will be two, and often three, matches a week, and he will not be back till seven o'clock. The time of "Hall", as dinner in Oxford is universally called, is usually six o'clock, but sometimes an hour later. To those unable to read after a full meal, [this] is a boon, for it allows them an extra hour before the brain is clouded . . .'

In the Lent Term of 1914 Harold Macmillan had won his Honours First in Classical Moderations. There followed 'the summer term of 1914. Eight weeks of bliss . . . As so often happens in times of England's greatest danger 1914 . . . was a glorious summer – day after day, week after week, of cloudless atmosphere with soft, voluptuous breezes and a Mediterranean sky. There were two years and more before Greats. There was little to be done but collect our books, to go – for form's sake – to a few lectures and to enjoy ourselves . . .'

During the summer weeks, as the term wore on, Macmillan and his friends 'played tennis and cricket, we punted, we bathed. We had luncheon and dinner parties. We lazed in the quad reading Dostoyevsky (who had just been discovered). Occasionally we went to London to the Russian opera and the ballet . . . We could only afford the gallery . . . I spoke at the Union . . . and was elected junior librarian – unopposed.

'At last it came to an end. But pleasure was only postponed. I had arranged to go again, with other friends to [a] . . . chalet [in the Haute Savoie] in the first week in August. Everything was prepared . . . Then the storm broke; the axe fell . . .'

Not far from Balliol was Magdalen where the Prince of Wales was an undergraduate. He returned there for the last time in May 1914, an informal figure in his preferred flannel trousers, fashionable turn-ups and casual sports coats. Despite the snobbish preening of the President of Magdalen, Sir Herbert Warren, who took the Prince in tutorials, he went, wrote a fellow undergraduate, 'with perfect simplicity to such public acts as the welcoming of the French President or a Garter ceremonial and then returned to Oxford with equal lack of ostentation'. The 'Pragger' as the undergraduates named him was noticeably more interested in sport than in scholarship. 'He played football eagerly and perseveringly,' continued the same writer in a June 1914 article in *The Times*, 'he became a private in the OTC; he played golf and ran with the beagles. He was a zealous spectator of college competitions and in Eights Week there was no more untiring follower of the boat from the tow path . . .' 'Bookish he will never be,' Sir Herbert Warren was forced to conclude in *his* report to *The Times* in November, but, countered the undergraduate, the Prince 'plunged at once into a catholicity of interests and achievements. He was entertained and gave entertainments in return; and those present found that, though he was at first thought shy, he was a delightful addition to a dinner party, most attractive in the quiet and humble part he took in the conversation, but full of humour and with opinions at once decided and sane. His laugh and smile are, perhaps, particularly attractive.' When war broke out in August he joined the Grenadier Guards and was seen at Oxford no more.

As Oxford went back to work so, in the first half of May, did the nation's schools. At Marlborough in Wiltshire a seventeen-year-old schoolboy Ulric Nisbet arrived for his last term, although he did not know it. The House where he was quartered was a new one built in 1911. In the then public school tradition he had been chosen for it by the Housemaster 'because I was thought to be good at games . . . In contrast to the primitive tubs in the older Houses, Field House provided up-to-date bathrooms and showers, and like every other part of the School it already emitted its own particular smell – one of terrific efficiency and cleanliness. We slept, fifty-six of us, in two long dormitories, one above the other . . . Early school started at seven. [The] seniors dressed carefully, and to enable them to be punctual without unnecessarily skimping their toilettes, [boys] took turns calling the time, first by minute, finally by quarter-minutes until the clock was on the point of striking, when time-keepers and laggards joined in the rush for classrooms.'

By May 1914 Ulric was himself a captain (prefect) with all the privileges over his juniors ('Sandy, my Housemaster, seldom intruded in our affairs') that this entailed. In Upper School – 'this barrack-room of ours, three quarters filled with rows of knife-eaten, time-darkened desks' – he held sway with the other captains at the captains' tables. There were in the room two fireplaces, 'one shared by eighty-five per cent of the occupants, the other exclusively reserved for the four captains and their friends'. The captains could administer beatings. The time-honoured message ran: 'You are wanted at the captains' table.' On the other hand, a well-inclined captain could save 'new bugs' from a variety of tests and tortures, including 'pull-throughs' on the hanging rings in the dormitory. The worst sin was to break the silence that greeted the captains' arrival in Upper School for evening prep at 7.15. Then 'every desk lid had to be flush with its frame, every sound suppressed; the penalty for non-observance, a public caning at the end of prep.

'To obtain victims [some] captains resorted to artifice. At the exact second when the school bell stopped its tolling . . . in they would charge with a gigantic broom and crash it upon the floor . . . Silence, immediate, absolute! Or did some voice break that silence? Had some desk lid been left a trifle open?' Ulric Nisbet's own excuse for beating an offender was somewhat more pertinent. '[The] recipient . . . brought it purposely upon himself by bicycling down the centre aisle of the room, crowned with a bowler, at the precise moment we entered . . . I had no desire to beat him; he was one of my best friends . . . Afterwards I walked with him to Chapel and told him of my regret. "Don't worry," he said. "They didn't hurt through three pairs of woollen pants."'

Field House, according to Nisbet, 'had a reputation for heartiness and a penchant for trophies that made us deservedly the most unpopular House in the School . . .' Apart from games and necessarily, work, food was the boys' main preoccupation.

'At breakfast we sat down to a bowl of thick porridge, an egg or a sausage, to which we added whatever our tuck-boxes or our pocket-money could run to. Lunch, attended by the whole school, commenced with a long Latin grace and continued with a roast of a shape and texture I have never met since. This was followed with the greatest regularity by a species of pudding known as "College Bolly" . . . It had the appearance of plum pudding, was in consistency bullet proof and, to give it a tasty look, arrived sprinkled with sugar. It was said by its detractors to contain all the scraps left over from breakfast. To these I was able to add other items from time to time, neither animal or vegetable . . . several pebbles of varying sizes; string, seldom more than a couple of inches in length, both white and brown; and the lower portion of a back collar stud . . . In Sandy's House the last meal of the day was Tea. True, a supper of hard biscuits and cheese was provided in Hall after evening Chapel, but we, Spartans in all things, were never allowed to partake of it. Our immediate rendezvous was House Classroom for the half-hour of second prep; and at ten o'clock we retired . . .'

For Bessie Ellis, in her very different life as a servant-girl in Kent, sleep came as soon as she crawled between the sheets in her attic bedroom. Each morning that summer she was up as soon as it was light, to clean the range and then set to work on the long scrubbed kitchen table. 'You put a lump of salt on it, then poured a kettle of boiling water over. That took the grease out. The floor was stone. There was no mop or anything. You got down on the sack – a "kneeler" – with a pail and brush.' At ten the gardener came into the kitchen for the day's order. The mistress rang up the butcher and fishmonger. She kept the keys to the store-cupboard. She would come and unlock it just to hand out some sugar or one pot of jam. We used to pray for her to lose the keys. You had to take a dish and go and ask to get enough rice to make a rice pudding for lunchtime. For cakes all the stuff was weighed out and you had to remember everything. Nothing was wasted either. It was used up thoroughly.

The mistress knew all about catering, quantities, recipes and such. She couldn't boil an egg but she could order a sumptuous dinner.'

To keep food fresh it was packed in blocks of ice delivered by the fishmonger, or stored in the larder with its slate slabs and the mesh on the windows which kept it cool. 'We kept things warm in a hay-box made by the carpenter, filled with hay or shredded news-paper, with a padded inside-lid. You'd put a stew on to boil and then put it in the nest for two or three hours. It worked a treat.'

The Brenchley vicarage made its own electricity which provided light but was 'never strong enough to work gadgets. We used to charge the pump for the electricity all night.' There was no laid-on water. It came from the pump or from barrels set out to catch the rainwater. This soft water was preserved for doing the laundry. As in so many other houses, Monday was wash-day when the village washerwoman called, and if there had been no rain, instructed 'Ellis' to draw from the well. 'We used Brobat for washing, strong-smelling stuff in a bottle. Almost everything we washed we starched, breaking down the lumps of starch with boiling water. The laundry itself was a room with a little round covered-in stove, heated with coke and with irons stood round it. We washed the clothes themselves in coppers heated by faggots of wood. Then they were rinsed out in blue and put through the wringer.'

Coppers were used also for boiling the bath-water. 'The gentry had hip-baths in their bedrooms. The housemaids carried hot water up to them from the copper in heavy brass pans. We had to have our hip-baths in the laundry. We put them in the middle of the room and closed all the windows. It was a real luxury, a hot bath. We had one, if we were lucky, once a week. We had no lavatory, just a bucket with a lid on up the garden.'

By the summer of 1914 Bessie or 'Ellis' as she was called, was a familiar part of the household. No longer imprisoned in the scullery, she had progressed upstairs. There she helped the housemaid dust and clean the main rooms. 'We put damp tea leaves on the carpet and swept them up with a long-handled broom. All the wood floors had to be polished so that they wouldn't stain.' But the vicarage children, three boys and a girl, were her main responsibility. 'It was my duty to keep them clean. Little devils they were. They used to collect sand beneath the kitchen window and throw it in.' Her reward was the granting of her request that she be taught to cook. 'We had an old cook. She used to drink a lot. She told me how to make pastry and when to stir things with a fork. If things didn't go right, she'd always say, they'd go wrong. She cooked a good dinner, mind. The cat would sit and wait for her afterwards outside the pub.'

On Sunday mornings the vicarage staff left the heavy iron pots and copper and brass pans simmering on the range while they attended their master at his place of work, in church. Amusements in such an isolated country district were scarce. 'We spent our spare time mostly sewing or knitting while someone read aloud to us, usually Dickens.' But there were trips on Bessie's afternoon off to Tunbridge Wells to shop in the carrier's cart. 'You bought sweets in twists of paper and biscuits loose. I went from one tin to another, getting so much from each. And making eyes at the chaps of course.' Then, 'the pictures were very nice, so quick they kept your attention. I tried to go every month but it cost 6d and I hadn't really got the money.' In Brenchley itself whist-drives were held in the village-hall. 'After it was over, if you'd played properly, there was dancing – the waltz, polkas, the lancers. I didn't know how to dance till I came to Brenchley.'

Up in London, in the very different ambience of ribbon-hung, flower-scented London ballrooms, the Season waltzed on, Lady Blythswood's smart dance at the Ritz being almost rivalled by the vast, grand dinner party Lady Cunard gave beforehand. Lady Curzon's ball (such splendour, sneered one diarist, for the grand-daughter of Levi Leiter of Chicago) saw all the dukes and duchesses, 'pretty girls in rows, all the smartest bachelors' dancing to Casano's Band surrounded by 'flowers by the million'. Lady Diana Manners danced too, in a frock reported as 'lovely and diaphanous' but 'in quantity perhaps just a little more reminiscent of her classical namesake than royalty, had it been present, might have approved.' Poiret's 'frail and fragmentary' Greek fashions were all the rage among her generation, with the more daring of them even going bare-legged to complete the effect. At Lady Clifden's Ritz dance a mass of rhododendron trees in full bloom provided 'a Futurist flare of colour'. Lady Granet countered with a party sprinkled with such celebrities as Mr Rudyard Kipling. Lady Dalkeith's ball at Montagu House was an altogether more sedate occasion but the paucity of vulgar floral decoration was made up for by a blinding display of ancestral gold and silver plate. The curious flocked to the Duke of Buccleuch's rarely-opened private mansion on the banks of the Thames, with its marble hall opening on to great reception rooms, their walls studded with famous works of art. In the warm night air the guests could wander by the river in the garden where Pepys once claimed to have seen Lady Castlemaine's lingerie fluttering in the breeze.

Pearl Barrington Crake spent the month meeting her fellow-debutantes.

'All the mothers had luncheon parties for their daughters. The girls would say things like, "I've just had my second tea party." And someone else would say, "How many girls turned up?" Those were the sort of things we talked about. Nothing important. There wasn't a cloud in our sky.

'Then all the mothers asked you to the various dinner parties. Those who didn't have enough money to give a dance spent their money on giving very nice dinner parties. My darling aunt and uncle asked me everywhere, knowing my mother could only "ask people in". On Sunday evenings we often had open house at Thurloe Square, so the young men used to come in for tea if they wanted to, and then we always used to have supper and my mother would say, "Up to eight can stay." At my coming-out dance my aunt had a house-party of twenty-five. All of the Scots Greys young officers were there so I knew them when I came to London.

'There was a lovely dance at Darlington House. And Londonderry House – I went to Lady Londonderry's party. It was a magnificent big house and always absolutely solid. Lady Londonderry was *the* great political hostess. I had tulle sleeves for my evening dress and going through the crush was so awful, trying to get into a door or something, and somebody's marvellous diamond brooch caught it and we were hung up for ages.'

As May in London rolled on with day after day of perfect weather, those who had energy to spare from the sleepless nights of dancing followed their own pursuits. The first spring meeting at Newmarket preceded the opening of the polo season, which saw Lord Wimborne fielding an American team to play the English on Leopold de Rothschild's ground at Gunnersbury Park. It was not a straightforward transatlantic contest. The Grenfell twins played for the Americans to stiffen their resistance and give practice to the English side.

Meanwhile the cricket season opened and boat-club elections were held. Female tennis players were beguiled into ordering their costumes by energetically-drawn advertisements in *Vanity Fair*. Five and a half yards of linen was considered decent coverage for the average female form – enough to make a narrow overtunic and skirt long enough to sweep the grass on the court. As if this were not enough encumbrance lawn vests were advised as well.

The bathing-beauties smiling out from *Vanity Fair*'s pages were similarly weighted down with clothes. They wore knickerbockers and over them a loose or belted wide-collared tunic. Their sleeves reached their elbows; ballet shoes laced to the ankle protected their feet; coloured tights and a matching hat completed the unwieldy ensemble. It was little wonder that most bathing-dresses, made of satin and silk, were never designed to go in water. To many fashionable women the concept of exercise meant no more than a noon-time stroll in Hyde Park; noon being the appointed hour for Society to show itself. Their husbands, armchair sportsmen during the Season's duration, meanwhile wistfully scanned the advertisements for shooting and fishing properties to let in the pages of *The Times*.

The Chelsea Flower Show of 1914 attracted more crowds than ever before. A feature of it was a competition for the best rock-garden, to be judged by Alfred Parsons R.A. Those whose interests were more artistic than horticultural were drawn to the great antiques sale which disposed of the Duke of Cambridge's property. Three Sheraton bow-front chests sold for the princely sum of £4 10/-. A Jacobean oak settle was knocked down for 3 guineas only. A Hepplewhite sideboard merited a higher bid of 10 guineas, but a Louis XIV occasional table could only raise £1 5/−. It was less even than the gilded Adam looking-glass at £2 15/-, or the lot of one hundred crystal glasses which fetched twice that.

Bidders from the sale no doubt attended the Summer Exhibition Private View at the Royal Academy. Prince Arthur of Connaught had addressed the traditional banquet and gained notice in *The Times* for his strong attack on 'perverted' modern art. Contemporary painting, he declared, was unbecomingly aggressive: it hid its violent message under the sacred name of art. Despite this pacifist stance the Duke's own speech resounded with military metaphors and made reference to the likes of Hannibal more than to the luminaries of art. But the exhibition *was* marred by violence, of an unexpected

[44]

kind. A suffragette ('an elderly woman of peaceable appearance,' said *The Times* in tones of injured surprise) slashed with a meat-cleaver the Sargent portrait of Henry James. Seized by the surrounding crowd, she announced her motive: to draw attention to women artists whose pictures fetched much less than Sargent's did. Although costly, the Sargent painting was not the most popular exhibit. This accolade went to a vast canvas depicting the gloomy end in the Antarctic of Captain Oates. Interest was aroused by individual portraits, including one of Lady Liberty, wife of the owner of the store. On the first day the newspapers reported the anachronistic appearance of an unknown old lady who, in the dress and black poke bonnet of the mid-Victorian era, came to view her grandson's picture on display.

Mark Hayler, although unemployed, was having an exceptionally happy summer. His parents, lively and independent themselves, were glad to see him with the time and leisure to explore the interests which they also shared. With his father he worked for temperance, for the Liberal Party and for women's suffrage. When they were not on the campaign trail, they attended lectures on such topics as the French Revolution, or listened to the Georgian poets read from their work at the Poetry Society's headquarters in Devonshire Street. 'My father,' says Mark Hayler, 'was a self-made man. He had hardly any schooling but he had a marvellous voice and he was adventurous. He became interested in social reform and even stood for Parliament. He kept his deposit when everyone else lost theirs. That summer he spoke frequently at meetings in places like Hackney Town Hall. He even shared the platform with several Liberal M.P.'s.'

Mark Hayler himself spent much time in the House of Commons and saw suffragettes chain themselves to its railings. 'Whenever they had a meeting there were always crowds and police. They were looked on as rather silly.' Nevertheless, he supported them, often attending rallies at Caxton Hall with his old employer, the 'radical countess'. 'In the teeth of her husband's opposition too. She was a great one. She went around addressing suffragette meetings. Meanwhile, he would be on another platform in another town making a totally contrary speech.' Every Monday, now he was unemployed, Mark Hayler went to King's Cross to meet off the train the Liberal M.P. for North Westmoreland. 'He opened his letters in the hansom cab going back to his house, and dictated replies while I took notes.' In May 1914 he went up to Newcastle to a great Liberal rally. 'Two M.P.'s had a debate on free trade and tariff reform and one thousand people filled the Town Hall every night for a week.'

The end of May passed in sadness with news of the sinking of the great ship, *Empress of Ireland*. With his sister Mark Hayler attended a memorial service for the six hundred Salvation Army officers who had lost their lives. 'It was in the Albert Hall. There were six hundred empty seats in the arena. Over each seat was a white sash. The theme was that we must take the place of all those who had died.'

For London Society May reached its traditional climax on the 27th, with the spectacle of the Derby followed by the Duchess of Devonshire's ball. By omnibus, by coach, by car, by charabanc, the public poured on to Epsom Downs – a record crowd of nearly four hundred thousand people. The traffic jams were of a length never experienced before, and spectators gawped curiously at the lines of motor-omnibuses parked alongside the gypsy caravans, tents and booths. The frock-coated King and Queen Mary in an ermine mantle watched their horse Black Jester lose to the twenty to one outsider Durbar II. The horse's owner, a Parisian named H. B. Duryea, gave a large party in the Berkeley grill-room where the tables were decorated in green and white, his racing colours.

Pearl Barrington Crake, who had motored down in a hired car with her uncle, a member of the Jockey Club, looked out from her seat in prestigious Number One Box on to a sea of colour. Against the green summer grass the women dressed in Paquin, Poiret and Worth bloomed like flowers, and flowers trimmed their spreading Watteau-shepherdess straw hats. Many of them carried this year's accessory, a matching parasol, the handle carved of rhino-horn or tortoiseshell and set with amethyst, topaz and semi-precious stones. Despite the blue skies others swaggered in swirling capes, modelled on Burberry's fashionable 'ancient Roman' look.

That evening Pearl's uncle dined at Buckingham Palace where the King gave his traditional Derby night dinner for the Jockey Club. By motorcade the diners then processed to Devonshire House where the Queen and the ladies of Society were waiting. At the top of the grand staircase, decorated with flowers and shrubs from Chatsworth, the Duchess of Devonshire received her guests. Through the red silk drawing-room, past the china displays and the Queen sitting waiting for a select few to be presented to her, they filed into the white and gold ballroom with its massive Rubens. Here while Pearl and her contemporaries danced on the newly-laid, shiny dance-floor, the King and Queen watched in state from two thrones in an alcove. The atmosphere lightened somewhat when they left long before the party's end at 2 a.m., having been served a light supper laid in the dining-room on solid gold plate.

In North Wales Violet Graham, who in her own words was 'supposed to be out', was experiencing a very different sort of season. In provincial society a debutante's coming out could amount to nothing more dramatic than a dinner given for her by the local squire. Occasionally the squire's wife would present a gift of pearls or a brooch to mark this unmomentous occasion. Violet Graham was luckier. The highlight of her summer would be the ball she would attend at Sandhurst at the end of July.

'At home I had nothing much to do. We had to make our own entertainment, me and my two sisters, one older, one younger. My brother was away at Wellington School. Education was considered more important for a boy, and Father had never approved of girls' schools. We went to Bath on shopping trips. We bought all our clothes in King's, the big shop there. Or we went to visit my aunt and two grandmothers, decorously dressed in hat and gloves.

'We did go away once early in the summer, to a pageant at Old Moreton Hall in Cheshire. It was on the theme of Queen Elizabeth and my cousins were also taking part. We were part of her retinue, dressed in white and gold dresses with Elizabethan ruffs and farthingales. There was a procession and singing and folk-dancing by the moat. The Welsh parsons dressed up as monks. They could all sing beautifully.

'Back home in the evenings we played cards or charades or dumb crambo. Mother read and tried to keep us quiet but it was a fair shindig. My older sister's mind was always on a book. We had to persuade her to join us. Everyone counts when you have to rely on people for your entertainment. Cousins and aunts and uncles frequently came to stay. They were always pushing food down us. They thought we looked frightfully peaky. We had been brought up in India where my father was in the army, and they said we were far too white and didn't eat enough.

[47]

'We weren't well off. My mother was a widow. We had no car for example. Our Welsh maid when asked about it, would reply with great dignity that we did not want anything so common as a car. Nevertheless, besides her, we had a cook and, most of the time, a governess, and a gardener. We made our own beds but we were not allowed to set foot inside the kitchen. I didn't learn to cook till after the war when we couldn't get anyone to do it for us.

'My younger sister was only fourteen and still in the schoolroom. She should have been having lessons but Mother had recently dismissed the German governess. She was a clever woman who made lessons interesting. There was no reason. Mother said later she had had a premonition.'

3

June

IN THE LAST WEEK OF MAY Rupert Brooke waited impatiently at his hotel in Greeley Square, New York, to take passage on the *Philadelphia*, the ship that would bear him home after his travels through America, Canada and the Pacific islands. 'I'm infinitely vigorous and excited,' he wrote to Eddie Marsh. 'I can't sleep for thinking of England.' In a letter from Washington to Cathleen Nesbitt, he lived out, part-jokingly, part-seriously, the moment when he would step on to English soil. 'I sail from New York on May 29,' he wrote, 'and reach Plymouth . . . Drake's Plymouth . . . where men speak softly and things are sold for shillings not dollars, and there is love and beauty and old houses, and beyond which are little fields, very green, bounded by small piled walls of stone – and behind them – the brown and black, splintered, haunted moor. By that the train shall go up – by Dartmouth where my brother was – I will make a Litany – by Torquay, where Verrall stayed, and by Paignton, where I walked in the rain; past Ilsham where John Ford was born, and Appledore, in the inn of which I wrote a poem against a Commercial Traveller; by Dawlish, of which John Keats sang; within sight of Widdicombe, where Uncle Tom Cobbley rode a mare; not a dozen miles from Galsworthy at Manaton; within sight, almost, of that hill by Drewsteignton on which I lay out all one September night crying. And to Exeter. And to Ottery St Mary, where Coleridge sojourned; and across Wiltshire, where men built and sang many centuries before the *Aquila* . . .' Typically, he was unable to resist a mischievously bathetic ending: 'Oh, noble train, oh glorious and forthright and English train, I will look round me at the English faces and out at the English fields, and I will pray . . . reach Plymouth, as I was saying when I was interrupted, on Friday June 5.'

'Will you be in London Friday night June fifth I shall,' ran the marconigram he sent to Eddie Marsh in London, to which came a laconic and prompt reply: 'Yes, Eddie.' And on June 5 Eddie Marsh, having dined with Cathleen Nesbitt and Denis Browne at the Queen's Restaurant in Sloane Square, took them to his flat to fill in time, and then to Paddington, where Brooke's train finally arrived at 2.45 a.m. And there was Brooke, sun-browned and sun-bleached ('rejuvenated and beachcomberish' he later described his new self), and carrying no doubt the huge straw hat with which he had mounted the *Philadelphia*'s gangway. He returned with them to Eddie Marsh's flat in Raymond Buildings, and spent what was left of the night in feasting and conversation.

Rupert Brooke had been a classics scholar at King's College, Cambridge, where his uncle was Dean. Brooke's father was a housemaster at Rugby. Brooke himself had access to the inner sanctums of the English intellectual elite: his childhood companions included members of the Stephen, Strachey and Woolf families, the founding spirits of Bloomsbury. He had grown up under the influence of his literary mother and his first enthusiasm had been for aestheticism and the decadent poets, Wilde and Swinburne (later, with a passion Baudelaire).

When he went to Cambridge, this changed. There the prevailing mood was to be modern (Virginia Woolf, never quite forgiving him for being anti-culture, called it 'a game . . . an amusing disguise'), to abhor the Victorians and the nineteenth century and to look forward to a bright, new age. Informality, naturalness and openness was the key. Being socialist was part of it, as was living in the country, shunning artifice or hypocrisy and, in Brooke's case, writing 'modern' verse, using everyday images as raw material for his poems. In a wryly affectionate review of these *Collected Poems*, which appeared in the *Times Literary Supplement* in August 1918, Virginia Woolf summed up this 'Grantchester' phase in Brooke's life, before his year-long trip to America and the South Seas in 1913. He was, she says, 'consciously and defiantly pagan. He was living at Grantchester; his feet were permanently bare; he disdained tobacco and butchers' meat; and he lived all day and slept all night in the open air. You might judge him extreme, and from the pinnacle of superior age assure him that the return to Nature was as sophisticated as any other pose, but you could not doubt that . . . he was an originator, one of those leaders who spring up from time to time and show their powers most clearly by subjugating their own generation. Under his influence the country near Cambridge was full of young men and women walking barefoot, sharing his passion for bathing and fish diet, disdaining book learning, and proclaiming that there was something deep and wonderful in the man who brought the milk and in the woman who watched the cows.'

Brooke 'came back to that wonderful cloudless June of 1914, quite dizzy,' recollected Cathleen Nesbitt, 'with thoughts of all he wanted to do. He wanted to see 1000 plays and walk 1000 miles and kiss 1000 girls and write 1000 poems . . . Rupert had what he called "a tearing hunger to do and do and do".' Eddie Marsh, his admirer and patron, who was also Winston Churchill's private secretary, put a London flat at his disposal and introduced him to social and political life in the capital. Before, Brooke's circle of upper-middle-class Fabians and young Cambridge intellectuals had not often crossed paths with London society. Now he would come to know such public figures as the Asquiths, and particularly the Prime Minister's daughter Violet, during this last London Season before the war.

On June 11 Brooke, having paid a brief visit to his home in Rugby, arrived back in London for a performance by Fokine and Karsavina at Covent Garden. It was a coveted experience. Since their first appearance in London in 1913 the Imperial Russian Ballet and Opera Companies had taken the city by storm. Already there were few seats to be had for any performance in their repertoire, although ten operas and fourteen ballets had been booked by Sir Thomas Beecham for the Theatre Royal, Drury Lane. On May 29 the Russian Opera Company had opened the season with Moussorgsky's *Boris Godunov*, a gorgeous production which evoked on stage all the colour and pageantry of a Tsar's coronation. 'Never since,' recalled Lady Diana Cooper in her autobiography, 'have we in England had our eyes so dazzled with new lights. The comets whizzed across the unfamiliar sky, the stars danced. The time-revered old Italian opera in its buskins and farthingales, its tights and its cap-doffing had wearied an audience older than me. Boxes at Covent Garden were hired for the season, but not for music. The darkness hid many sleepers. Wagner nights were more musically alert, because only enthusiasts could stand them. Now came a blast to awaken the dead, a blaze of blinding gold, the Kremlin bells clanged and clashed, and Boris was there, a humble giant on his way to be crowned . . .'

The 'giant' in reality was far from humble. At 6' 4" the towering figure of the Russian opera star Feodor Chaliapin was fêted that Season wherever he chose to go. Society music-lovers like the distinguished, grey-haired Lady Ripon, herself of Russian ancestry, fought each other to invite him to their soirées – Lady Cunard and Muriel Draper, resplendent in gorgeous jewelled turbans, made attendance at the opera almost obligatory for the fashionable world. At the June reception given for Richard Strauss's fiftieth birthday Chaliapin was there, as well as Debussy, Stravinsky, Karsavina and Sir Thomas Beecham. Meanwhile, the playing of Casals and Rubinstein could be heard drifting through the open windows of Muriel Draper's drawing-room. Debussy too gave impromptu concerts – at Lady Speyer's eclectically-furnished house in Grosvenor Street, where furniture from Marie Antoinette's boudoir nudged heavy German wood-carvings and Persian tiles. Strauss accompanied his violin-playing hostess on the piano in Lady Speyer's music-room which overlooked a small courtyard with a Renaissance fountain. Lady Speyer's neighbours in the surrounding 'mean streets', if Osbert Sitwell is to be believed, did not appreciate such music-making. On one such evening, when an Alpine band had clashed and tinkled their way through a ponderous Tyrolean repertoire, a shower of fish-heads and rotten eggs sailed over her wall to land on her unsuspecting guests. 'The first casualty,' recalled Osbert Sitwell with some relish, 'was Sir Claude Phillips, a rotten egg exploding on the large pearl stud which held together his expansive and exquisitely laundered shirt front as he lingered outside, by the tethered water-lily.' But it was Diana Manners who won the homage of the great Chaliapin, receiving bows from him as he stood in the glare of the spotlights on stage. He sent flowers to her box and encouraged her in yet more daring escapades, including the occasion when disguised as a peasant she joined the chorus for one performance. 'My head was turned,' she admits, 'and I behaved outrageously.' Nevertheless, she took comfort from the thought that she shielded the great man in part from the advances of 'rapacious women'. Chaliapin's other female admirers, who numbered half of London Society, were unamused when she forbade him to attend a party where she was not invited.

On June 15 a performance of Rimsky-Korsakov's *Le Coq d'Or* brought together the two great Russian companies of opera and ballet. From rows of petunia-robed choristers, arranged tier upon tier, soloists stepped forward to sing an accompaniment to the dancers. June 23 marked the debut of the Imperial Russian Ballet's newest and youngest star – Leonide Massine, brought in at seventeen to replace the great Nijinsky. He was playing the title role in Diaghilev's last and most lavish pre-war production *Légende de Joseph*, costumed by Bakst and with music by Richard Strauss. Diaghilev had choreographed the part as a vehicle for Nijinsky but substituted Massine in a jealous rage at Nijinsky's marriage. On to a set 'halfway between Babylon and Venice' with marble floors, huge twisting gold columns, fountains and crystal bowls piled high with fruit, Massine as Joseph the shepherd-boy was borne wrapped in yellow silk on a litter. Here in front of the *corps de ballet* dressed as exotic slaves, their numbers swelled for this production by two Russian wolfhounds and a group of enormous mulattoes bearing golden whips, he danced the dance of innocence that would supposedly arouse the passions of this jaded court. The audience found themselves aroused more by the sheer spectacle than by the music which was generally considered dull and second-rate. The war poet Siegfried Sassoon, watching his first ballet with a returned ticket obtained on the prompting of Edward Marsh, found the performance over-elaborate and a failure. He was equally bemused, it must be said, by the other part of the programme – all white tutus and lilting music – and had to wait until it was over to discover its title: Chopin's *Les Sylphides*.

However, having had his first taste of Russian theatricality, Sassoon became an eager visitor to the Imperial Opera and Ballet, though he displayed a distaste for the fashionable audiences, 'patronising the arts with shallow sophistication'. Osbert Sitwell, for all his own hectic socialising, saw the point of Sassoon's reservations. On June 18 after a performance of Stravinsky's *Le Rossignol*, he watched the slight, abstracted figure of the conductor walk out on stage and bow to an audience of 'clustered, nodding tiaras and white kid gloves'. Such glamour, according to Sitwell, was suspect in the eyes of *avant-garde* intellectuals like Roger Fry. As a result music-lovers very often shunned these galas while the fashionable world flocked to attend.

The influence of Bakst and Benois, of the extravagant orientalism of Russian costumes and stage-design, travelled far and wide. A Russian theme grew noticeable in pre-war fashion. It became commonplace in the summer of 1914 to see women in turbans to match their evening clothes. The Russian craze spread to contemporary house furnishings also. In 1954 ballet critic Richard Buckle writing a catalogue piece to accompany the Diaghilev Exhibition he had organized, claimed that even then there could still be seen 'lampshades in Scottish boarding-houses which owe[d] their existence to *Shéhérazade*'. Osbert Sitwell noted an attempt to imitate Russian spectacle in the expensive, extravagant parties of 'that flowering summer'. Each ball outdid the last, and for a presentable young officer like himself there could be as many as five or six such entertainments any one night. As the guests danced to the music of not one but sometimes two or three bands, 'electric fans whirling on the top of enormous blocks of ice buried in banks of hydrangeas' served to keep them cool. All around was '. . . a profusion of full-blooded blossoms: of lolling roses and malmaisons, of gilded musical-comedy baskets of carnations and sweet-peas . . . huge bunches of orchids, bowls of gardenias . . . flat trays of stephanotis . . .' 'There were really terrific sit-down suppers,' remembers Pearl Barrington Crake. 'There was no such thing as a fork supper.' At Derby House, Lansdowne or Londonderry House, at Bridgewater House or Stafford House, 'all magnificent, gilded and marbled', the gardens were set with striped marquees and fairy lights dotted along the winding paths. Flowers edged the stairs and decked the suppertables, which groaned under the tonnage of lobsters, quails, strawberries, ices, figs, nectarines and hot-house peaches. Champagne bottles stood row upon row on the sideboads, although young girls were not expected to sample more than one glass. 'Dances are longer as well as nicer than they were,' claimed a letter-writer to the June 1914 issue of the *Tatler*. 'Most of 'em begin with dinner – that's so as to be certain of one's men . . . And without the five o'clock kippers, kidneys and beer, whose succulent savour rouses even the sleepy chaperone from her secret slumbers, no really smart dance is counted as done tophole.' 'You'll come to my little party?' a *Tatler* columnist parodied the 1914 hostess. 'And when you do go along you find a marquee in the garden, Casano's band busy and tom tits' toes on toast with the Bollinger for supper.'

At these functions, recalls Diana Manners in her autobiography, elderly ladies took the floor with 'dear old prancing partners jangling with orders and decorations and with coat-tails flying'. Ranged round the room on upright chairs, the chaperons studied their well-bred charges, 'young girls', according to Diana Manners, 'raw and shy, innocent of powder and on the whole deplorably dressed, with their shapeless wispy hair held by crooked combs'. Gloves for both sexes were mandatory – 'and which of us could afford a new pair nightly? So the not-so-new were worn and we often reeked of cleaning petrol. Shoes were of pink or white satin and were smudged after the first dance by clumsy boys' boots.'

In between each dance, 'a sort of slave or marriage market' gathered at the door, with the most popular girls triumphantly juggling partners on 'ball cards with dear little pencils. Everybody had these programmes,' remembers Pearl Barrington Crake, 'and they came up and asked you to dance. When you didn't want to and they came and asked you, you put the most wonderful sort of hieroglyphics down on your card. And when you did, you wrote the person's name over the hieroglyphics. And then you talked while the band had stopped, so you were very happy.' When the music started again, giving mothers and chaperones a chance to distinguish, and glare or smile at each prospective beau, a sad trickle of wallflowers sought the inconspicuous shelter of the cloakrooms.

In Diana Manners' mother's day, her group of friends, the 'Souls', had earned Gladstone's approbation for bringing together the two political parties at social gatherings. Liberals and Conservatives mingled easily together. In the early years of the century Balfour could still arrive at receptions arm in arm with his political opponent, Asquith, after they had spent an afternoon of sarcastic interchange across the floor of the House.

Now the Home Rule crisis was souring this amicable arrangement. On May 21, 1914, under Liberal auspices, the Home Rule Bill for Ireland went to the Commons for its Third Reading. The Conservatives were up in arms. London Society was divided, drawing-room against drawing-room. The political hostesses did battle against each other. The Conservative Marchioness of Londonderry would not even enter a house where Home Rulers were lurking. Lord Curzon gave a ball and invited his sovereign but not the Liberal Prime Minister. Margot Asquith met with 'icy vagueness' from the Tory ladies in the Speakers Gallery. The atmosphere at such 1914 political receptions was described in cynical terms by an anonymous writer in June *Vanity Fair*. He chose as his venue 'an unpretentious street in Mayfair . . . [The] houses' exteriors would not suggest to any save the initiated the possibility of either spaciousness or luxury within . . .' He goes on to take us through a typical 'Night in the

Season' in which an energetic hostess whose husband has political pretensions, is entertaining for her party.

'A taxicab turns the corner, takes its place in the long file of motors, cabs and broughams that halt for a brief space before an open door from which a red carpet ranges to the edge of the curb. On the other side of the street fifty yards higher up another reception is in progress, so a seemingly endless stream of vehicles is passing in opposite directions. The night is warm and cloudless, many windows are open and there is a faint odour of unseen flowers.

'Past the portals men and women part company and seek the cloakrooms, to meet again in a few moments free from wraps. Then we move to a broad marble staircase, with its flowers and greenery on either side, and at the head of the stairs, by the first of the reception rooms, we are welcomed by our hostess . . . whose jewels shine and twinkle in the brilliant light . . . Many are before and behind us, but the lady of the house . . . contrives to compress into a word and a movement a suggestion that our coming is a matter of general satisfaction to her . . . the thing is done perhaps a couple of hundred times between eleven and midnight . . . [although] many of the visitors are friends of friends and personally unknown to their entertainers.

'The reception rooms, three in number, are *en suite*, and there is a music-room beyond. The floors are bare and highly polished; the electric lights set in the moulded ceilings flood the whole place . . . Slowly . . . the guests split up into groups, and passing from one to another . . . one hears all the affairs of *le monde* . . . discussed from a standpoint that never reaches the world outside. It is the hour of gossip, daring, often witty and always well-informed . . . The hostess is a staunch Unionist . . . and if you walk from one end of those spacious rooms to the other you will not see a solitary representative of Liberalism. You will find half a dozen men who look to hold Cabinet rank in the near future, and two or three who have held it in the comparatively recent past, but of the party in power, not a sign. It is the social law of 1914 that there shall be no mixing of political circles, and though many with friends in either camp may complain, the fiat has gone forth.'

The writer continues with an exposé of his fellow-guests: 'That radiant woman still young and chattering gaily is in the throes of serious domestic troubles . . . She finds no pleasure in being here, but to be away would be to provide harsh tongues with fresh currency . . . The tall athletic man, who looks as though he had never known misfortune, has taken refuge with moneylenders from the disasters of the racecourse . . . That young and rather weak-looking lad, heir to a great title, has lost a fortune at one of London's private gambling-houses less than a mile away.' A respected politician is incoherent as a result of brandy. A middle-aged dowager has arrived with her 'friend', a cosmopolitan gentleman, helping her make large sums on the Stock Exchange. 'By her is a pretty foreign woman "run" by certain ladies. They take her out [in Society], and she pays for all the frocks.

'Singers from the opera-houses have now arrived and a move is made to the music-room . . . The guests crowd round the miniature platform without checking their conversation or even greatly reducing its tone.' But the tenor and the soprano sing 'with the full strength of their brazen lungs. They are imperturbable. The guests cannot drown them. They must cease for a moment to utter words that cannot be heard. It is too much, this gross interference with the liberty of unmusical people, and nearly half the guests go downstairs to the supper-room. There little flower-decked tables are served by correct impassive waiters, with all manner of luxuries not yet in season that might be calculated to tempt soon after midnight appetites that were satiated less than four hours ago. For the middle-aged men there is a smoking-room where they can enjoy a choice cigar and a whisky. Those who give readiest ear to the music are women – the proportion to men must be as three to one – but even for them the concert is short enough; it is over within the hour at a cost of running far into three figures.'

Pearl Barrington Crake's chief memory of June was of her presentation at court. At the beginning of the month she had taken part in this ceremony which set the seal on her coming-out. Her hair up, plumed with ostrich feathers, and wearing a cream beaded court-dress, she curtsied to the King and Queen at one of the two last courts (and some said most glittering of all) before the war. Her long train had, appropriately, a motif of Alexandra roses. 'Hours of work by the embroiderers and tireless Miss Thorpe, who had Mummy's court dress to fit as well.' On the night of June 4, Pearl joined the hundreds of debutantes gathered in Buckingham Palace Hall. Hundreds more waited with their mothers, their fathers and brothers – uniformed or in black velvet court-dress – in the tail of cars outside, which snaked all the way back along the Mall. Up the red-carpeted staircase twined with red and white roses and lined with Yeomen of the Guard, they made their way through the Picture Gallery and three State Drawing-Rooms. A roll of drums announced the start of what the American Ambassador Walter Hines Page, described as, 'the best-managed, best-mannered show in the world' as, preceded by the Lord Chamberlain, the Royal Family advanced through a ripple of curtseys to the dais. Over them hung a canopy retrieved from the Indian Durbar; alongside were the King's Indian orderlies, and before, every uniform that the Empire could boast. To one side of the throne, a circle of duchesses watched the presentation of the *Corps Diplomatique*. Then to the accompaniment of soft music, the main ceremony began. For two hours a file of debutantes and older women waited to pass before the dais. Their moment when it came was brief: a deep curtsey for which they received a brisk regal nod. The American Ambassador, bemused by the jewels and coronets, the scarlet-suited pages, gaudy rajahs, and court chamberlains in white and gold, declared himself to be 'distinguished' in 'waiter-black'. He was amused particularly by the inappropriate figure cut by the President of the Board of Trade. 'Old John Burns stands just across the way in more gilt than any but a strong working-man could carry.' In mid-ceremony one young girl, a suffragette, dropped to her knees before the King. 'Your Majesty, for God's sake . . .' Two gentlemen-at-arms were there before she could end the sentence. She was marched out and, as if nothing had happened, the queue filed on. Nevertheless, her mother, when she heard the news, fainted, while for that day the King's diary entry was sour: 'I don't know what we are coming to.'

In June, too, the King and Queen went down to inspect the cadets at the Royal Military Academy at Woolwich. It was the summer term. Cadet Sergeant Cyril Drummond was in his second year. 'In a way I was a silly little boy. I didn't work hard enough at the beginning and I dropped maths in my first term. I got in in January 1912, the year – luckily for me – they extended the course and took in an extra big batch, a double term. But I was away the whole of the autumn of 1913. A gun had gone off through my hand that summer in Norfolk at my parents' home. I was Captain of the Revolver Team too, would you believe?

'The King and Queen came to see "The Shop", as we cadets called it, in the summer term 1914. They laid on a big show for them and for Princess Mary. The King, mounted on a horse, was to take the salute and see a six-gun battery of the Royal Field Artillery do their stuff with the eighteen-pounders. Then he was to walk through to the back where the six-inch guns were mounted on a coastal battery site. There was to be a display there of which I was in charge. After that there would be a full-dress ceremonial parade.

'When the day came, the padre sitting next to me at breakfast announced there was to be no six-inch gun display. The King had declined to get off his horse. He was going to stay put in front. I had to dash back to my quarters and change out of my canvas into tunic, helmet, gloves, pipeclad belt, the lot – and then get back in time to fix bayonets and march past, quarter column, with the band playing, and then halt and present arms. When it was over, the King rode out followed by the Queen and Princess Mary in a carriage looking as grim as death. They went to Woolwich Common where the entire garrison was on parade and we marched past again. Then the Royalty were set to go to Woolwich Mess, the Royal Military Mess, for a slap-up luncheon. There was to be a photograph with all the officers, and the King was laughing with General Phipps-Hornby, the Commander of the Royal Artillery, while the photographer was bobbing in and out of his black cloth in readiness. Suddenly the Queen's clear voice cut across everybody: "Do hurry up, George. You're keeping everyone waiting."'

Cyril Drummond did not come from a military background. His father, who had recently moved to Norfolk from Leigh, near Blackheath, was a country vicar. When the Woolwich term broke up at the end of July, Cyril was fully intending to spend the summer in East Anglia. 'I knew I was going to have to work damn hard in the summer vacation to make sure of getting a Field Artillery commission. I was still having trouble with my hand too. I could mount on a horse without stirrups but I couldn't stand on my hand in gym. One morning when the chaps in the gym were standing a bit easy, the Staff-Sergeant put us all on sick parade. There was the biggest parade there had ever been marching down to the cadets' hospital which was on the road past the common. The MO, an RAMC Major, was jolly fed up with all these chaps swinging the lead. We were in Six Company, and we were the last. He barked at me: "Now, what's the matter with you?" Then he looked at my wrist. He worked my hand about a bit and then said, "You can't move all your joints. This raises the question of whether or not I can recommend you for a commission." I said, "Well, I can ride perfectly well." He replied, "You're supposed to be able to move all your joints." Finally, I asked, "Shall I write my people and get the photograph that was taken to show you what is wrong?" "Yes," he said. "Write away for it."

'That weekend at Woolwich I was out of my mind. I felt I ought to get out before they kicked me out, and then at least I could go into the Special Reserve. The photograph came the following morning, and I went down and showed it to him. He must have been in a better temper because he said quite casually, "I don't see anything wrong with it. But you'd better come down to me and we'll treat it with hot and cold water." I did this all through the summer term, and whether I was going to stay in the Army or not always depended on his mood – whether he was optimistic or depressed.

'I knew I'd got to pull my place up anyway. Only the first fifteen out of us had their choice of corps. Most became sappers, the remainder RFA or RHA depending on their horsemanship marks. I'd pulled up thirty places that summer term but I had to get higher in the autumn. I was looking forward to a hard time of it in the senior term.'

Hilda French was having a hard time of it already. In the summer of 1914 she was working again. 'How we worked though. We really worked. I was a little domestic maid for a Mrs Lee in Latchmere Road. I had gone on from the range and washing to tablework and silver. We had half a day off a week and every other Sunday afternoon. Once a month we got a whole day. You'd have thought they were giving you the keys to heaven. I was so elated when I could get out. I loved the country and the open air. It was like a prison inside those stuffy houses. Girls in Holloway Prison now have more freedom than what I had in those days. We had heard of the

[60]

suffragettes. We thought they were mad though. They didn't seem to us to have anything to do with us.

'My sister worked not far away and we went to the Kingston or the Richmond Empire. Or we would go and meet some lads down by the river. We all met by the bandstand first, the girls and boys. There were gangs from Surbiton, Richmond, Ham. We girls would sit on the seats and talk to them and they'd walk us home together. Till you got a serious one. I spotted mine at once and said, "He's mine." His name was Frederick Joseph Felstead. We made our own games up. We played kiss-in-the-ring. You'd push a girl in. We kept pushing each other in. The first time he took me home was 1914. I was sixteen. I said to my Ma, "I've got a young man. Can I bring him home?" She said, "Ask your Pa." He said, "You do. Let me have a look at him." I dressed up to kill in a black velvet hat and a cerise pink costume. I always loved clothes. They said I always had a needle in my hand. Anyway, they liked him. From then on we done our courting. We walked and talked and had a good laugh. My young man was the biggest flirt. I don't know how he sorted me. I expect his mother said, "I don't like that Flossie. I like Hilda."'

Despite her burgeoning hopes of marriage to Fred Felstead, June 1914 saw Hilda French reconciling herself to the hated life of service. 'What else was there? I never imagined myself making munitions and stuff.'

On June 5 there had been another Court at Buckingham Palace, followed by a ball on June 9 and on June 10 a levée. Officials circulated the state reception rooms, asking guests to show their tickets. 'It was astonishing,' commented one disgruntled Englishman, 'for visitors to see how a handful of "wild women" could keep the English Court on tenterhooks.' But, suffragettes or not, the Court's contingent of European society was larger than ever this year. Buckingham Palace, an experienced and jaded courtier was heard to observe, was 'as crowded as a lunch-tent at Lords'.

Some had avoided the set quadrilles and stuffy royal formality to celebrate at Eton on the 4th of June. Eton's 'Glorious Fourth' traditionally drew large crowds of parents, sisters, uncles and aunts and friends. Princess Mary came to visit her brother Prince Henry, the King's third son. Also present was Lady Desborough, whose uncharacteristically modest view it was that, 'mothers should be seen but heard as little as possible at Eton'. In a bobbing sea of 'silk hats and sunshine', muslin, chiffon, parasols and lace, 'waves of visitors' swept into the chapel; to School Yard; to hear Latin speeches; to watch cricket on the quaintly-named Agar's Plough; and finally, thankfully, take refuge at the luncheon tables. At the Headmaster's side, a group of Westminster boys sat, a relic of the days when they had rowed on the Fourth against Eton. And afterwards, as shady-hatted collectors sold roses for charity on the lawn ('Freckles,' Helena Rubinstein had warned them, 'are an affection ... With nut-brownness [goes] a ring in the nose, black teeth and tattooed chin'), the afternoon passed amidst sunshine and the scent of strawberries. At 6.30 came its highlight, the procession of boats with their flower-decked, fancy-dressed crews. Until at last fireworks flared briefly and brilliantly in the summer evening.

And there were still the other great outdoor festivals of the Season to come. On the morning of Derby Day, during Ascot week or Henley, the staff of Fortnum and Mason rose before 4 a.m. to prepare the luncheon-boxes for their customers. At the appointed hour a great queue filled the surrounding streets, as cars and motor-omnibuses arrived to collect each hamper. If they were lucky it would include caviare brought three times weekly direct to Piccadilly from Astrakhan.

The week before Ascot was, wrote a 1914 social columnist, 'the very thick and height of the Season ... The great society race-meeting strikes the top note in that crescendo of social happenings which begins with the April showers and comes to a full stop with Cowes.' This year, the writer noted snobbishly, had seen 'a strenuous struggle to separate the sheep from the goats, and keep the royal enclosure not only a little less tightly packed than usual, but also as pure as the lily in the dell'. Even so, the 'actressocracy' was there in numbers. 'Wonderful to see how quickly they pick up the jargon of their new environment.'

Ascot week had begun in a climate that was uncertain meteorologically and politically. On the first day of the meeting it was cold enough to ensure that even the most fashionable wore furs and motor-cloaks over their race-going clothes. Those few who did brave the elements, like Lady Granard in a gown of silver-embroidered white net, drew the crowd's attention more for their frozen posture than for any elegance of dress. Still, the majority, warm in cloaks and motor-capes, found these a drawback too, as immaculately-dressed detectives subjected them to body-searches for concealed weapons. Inside the Royal Enclosure, coats left on seats were bundled off unceremoniously to the nearest police-station: 'All our poor little wraps and things.' 'The spectre of the hammer and the bomb,' boomed one affronted race-goer, 'was an ever-present anxiety. Will the Suffragettes, one wonders, still be keeping . . . Society on tenter-hooks, say in the Season of 1917?' Gold Cup Day on June 18 brought at last more clement weather. On a brilliant day, four queens, including Queen Mary, her emeralds glowing against her gold and silver dress, watched the King's colt *Sunny Lake* run to victory.

Victory came too in the Ladies' Singles at Wimbledon for the indomitable Mrs Lambert Chambers, already holder of the 1911 and 1913 titles and one of the few mothers ever to win. The defending Men's Champion, A. F. Wilding, suffered a reverse, however, when he was beaten by the Australian player, Brooks. But the star of the championships was Mr Wilding's protégé, Suzanne Lenglen, whom he had coached on the Riviera to become Ladies' Champion of France. Petite, with blue-ribboned hair and a flapper frock, and carrying the 14-ounce racket which she had picked up for the first time only three years before, Madamoiselle Lenglen was the darling of the Wimbledon crowd. But she was a baseline player, a superb rallyer but weak at net, and here the stocky strength of Mrs Chambers, conventional in her long, full white skirt, long-sleeved shirt and sober tie, was certain to triumph.

By late June, the pace of the Season was already dwindling. 'Balls and parties fixed for July one can almost count on one hand,' bemoaned a social columnist whose champagne and *foie gras* such balls obviously were. But the month had seen two of 1914's most extravagant and successful charity affairs: the Anglo-American Peace Centenary Ball (with an 1814 procession), and the fancy-dress Midnight Ball at the Savoy Hotel. The Peace Ball, as its participants noted ironically only a month or so afterwards, was a celebration of one hundred years of peace among the English-speaking nations. 'Exactly one hundred years will have passed,' ran its programme, 'on Christmas Eve 1914, since the signing of the Treaty of Ghent, which formally closed the war of 1812 . . . In celebrating the Centenary of Peace, the countries that have given birth to Shakespeare and Lincoln, Milton and Penn . . . are setting a magnificent example to the rest of the civilised world.' In this mood of confident nationalism, the Albert Hall, where the ball was to begin at 10 o'clock, was decorated with hanging baskets and flowers in red, white and blue. For the Americans, lest they feel outdone, there was a replica of *Santa Maria*, Columbus's ship. Exactly at midnight the doors of the ballroom opened to reveal to the startled ball-goers a curious procession. Mrs John Astor led, dressed as the District of Columbia, partnered by Britannia, and in their wake a trail of other States and Dependencies. The 'Puritans' processed in shockingly worldly white organdy muslin collars. Boadicea was noticeable for her breast-plate; an extraordinary 'aborigine' for little else but ostrich feathers. 'Red Indians'; pukka Indian ranees in sarees of blue and crimson; South African 'settlers' weighed down with diamond chains and head-dresses of gold brought up the rear of the procession.

On the 25th June the Midnight Ball in aid of the National Institute for the Blind took place at the Savoy Hotel. It was a costume ball, beginning with supper, naturally enough at 12 p.m. Among the Persian nobles, Watteau shepherdesses and Venetian courtiers, Lady Diana Manners stood out in a unique hybrid costume. The *Daily Graphic*, at a loss to describe it, drew attention instead to her 'coronet of glowing poinsettias and long pointed red morocco shoes'. The *Daily Telegraph*, equally perplexedly reported that, 'with a tiara and, depending on it a long veil of red, [she] carried a red wand.' As they entered the star-spangled ballroom, male guests were presented with suede cigar-cases filled with gold-tipped cigars. Their ladies received white leather note-pads encrusted with gold. Soldiers from Woolwich Arsenal waited at table, while pretty actresses and girls from the musical comedy stage served the drinks. The stars of their profession were present too. Thirty of them, including Ruby Miller and the young Cicely Courtneidge, agreed to be auctioned off as dancing partners. There were more substantial prizes on offer as well. A Daimler was one of them, won appropriately by a doctor from Moorfields Eye Hospital. A fifty-guinea Paquin evening dress was raffled, along with twenty guinea hats, two aeroplane flights, antiques, jewellery, exquisite lingerie and Venetian glass. In the early hours when outside the hotel the pavements were thronged with gypsies, pierrots, futurists, even a futurist Apache, a group of revellers borrowed a cart from Covent Garden to bear themselves and their booty home. The headline over the *Daily Sketch*'s account of the ball in next morning's paper was a laconic: 'Nobody Bored.'

None of the private balls could rival this, but Mrs John Astor's

Chelsea Flower Show, May 19th 1914.

Hulme, Manchester. A may-pole in the slums.

Revellers leaving the Midnight Ball at the Savoy Hotel, June 1914.

Diana Manners and Nancy Cunard.

dance almost did, the dresses being reported on as worthy almost of Buckingham Palace itself. Lady Cunard came in white brocade bound in silver, her daughter Nancy (having lost the battle with her mother for once) in shell-pink satin, roses perched demurely in her hair. Nancy had chosen pink too for her Court presentation, a pale pink tulle dress with a train of rose-petals. Later she received an invitation to a garden-party, but unlike Pearl Barrington Crake, not to a royal ball. Lady Cunard still was not approved of by Queen Mary. In her pink dress Nancy Cunard went on instead to the Countess of Huntingdon's Claridge's party, where everything was pink, from the hostess's gown to the satin ribbons hanging from the ceiling. Amidst this pink miasma, the Duchess of Marlborough stood out in pristine white, emphasised by 'ropes and ropes' of creamy pearls. Lady Drogheda, avant-garde as ever, wore a gown 'composed of hanging fringes of beads, which is much the fashion at the moment', reported an observer. Walking with a stick and hampered by an injured ankle, Lady Curzon held court in a corner of the room, her small golden head, recalled Diana Manners, crowned with her favourite torquoise crown. It could not quite compare with Buckingham Palace, where the Queen's Koh-i-Noor diamond sparkled in her crown, but it was, decided the *Daily Express* commenting admiringly on the dinner for eighty beforehand, 'a very smart affair'.

At dawn, as rubber-clad workmen hosed down the London streets, Diana Manners remembers 'red-breasted, top-hatted' linkmen hailing her a cab. A married chaperone supposedly undertook to escort her home, but daylight often found her creeping alone across the cobbled courtyard to her door, her feet in their pointed shoes, aching from six punishing hours of continuous dancing. But with no work to call her forth next morning, she could 'count eight on [her] fingers from whatever time it was. Then I jotted, "Call me at ten-eleven-twelve" on the pad that hung on my bedroom door.'

The Rutlands' house, now the Overseas League, in Arlington Street, was a huge mansion, 'one of the most unspoilt 18th century London houses'. An arched gate-way and gate-house led into its private yard. The nine servants and visiting tradesmen travelled by underground passage between lodge and kitchens so as to keep discreetly hidden from ducal eyes. Inside the house's main front door, a pillared hall contained a balustraded stone staircase. At the back, secondary stairs retained their outwardly curving bannisters designed to leave room for crinolines. At the back too were the great William Kent reception rooms overlooking Green Park. In the vast ballroom young men who called were entertained to tea.

Some of these young men Diana Manners had first met six years before when she was still a child of fourteen. In the summer of 1908 she had stayed at Brancaster in Norfolk with the family of the famous actor-manager Sir Herbert Beerbohm Tree. His three exotic daughters Viola, Felicity and blonde, bohemian Iris were her fast friends. A nearby house held a group of young Oxford undergraduates on a reading party: among them were Charles Lister, Edward Horner and Patrick Shaw-Stewart. This was Diana Manners' first encounter with the 'doomed group of young men' whose friendship, she claimed later in her autobiography, had such a strong influence on her. The rest of their circle – the Grenfell brothers, the Asquiths, Denis Anson – she came to know better later, when as a debutante bored with hunt-balls, shooting-parties and rich, dull eligible eldest sons, she launched herself on a 'primrose path of dalliance'. House-parties, sketching-parties, moonlight poetry recitals, after-dinner drives in open racing-cars, 'swimming in cool river pools with Grenfell gods', there seemed no reason during this early summer of 1914, why life should not go on in this intoxicating way for ever.

Trees, Grenfells, Manners, Horners, Listers, Asquiths – this group of young friends, the Coterie as they had christened themselves, were many of them the children of that earlier society clique, the Souls. The Souls had drifted together in the late 1880's and 1890's and become a close-knit, exclusive group. They thrived on wit, conversation (hence their nickname from Lord Charles Beresford who complained of them sitting around and talking about their souls), and their speciality, the games played in country-house drawing-rooms after dinner, in which they liked to show off their cultivation and erudition. They were young, bright, the women stylish and the men able. Many of them like Arthur Balfour and George Curzon had already made their mark politically.

The Coterie were not at all political. On the contrary, they reflected, according to Diana Manners, one of the best known among them, the spirit of Baudelaire, of Aubrey Beardsley, of Max Beerbohm and the *Yellow Book*. 'Our pride,' she remembers, 'was to be unafraid of words, unshocked by drink, and unashamed of "decadence" and gambling . . .' Coterie members recited Swinburne to one another. They cultivated a private language with its own vocabulary. They referred to themselves as the 'Corrupt Coterie', glorying in the disapproval they evoked in society's stuffier corners. 'Our peak of unpopularity,' Diana Manners recalled truthfully, 'was certainly 1914 and 1915.'

The centre of the Coterie was the Prime Minister's cleverest son, Raymond Asquith. He was the oldest of the group, a married man of thirty-six when war broke out, a barrister and a Fellow of All Souls. He had a reputation for coruscating wit which made him popular amongst twenty-year-olds like Diana Manners. 'Happiness was never complete if [Raymond] was not there,' she recalls. Though 'ten years older than the eldest of us . . . he was the most discipled and loved.'

Katharine Asquith, Raymond's pale, striking wife, Diana also admired. She was Katharine Horner, daughter of Sir John Horner, a scholarly baronet who had instilled in her his love of books and learning. Her father cherished his quiet, contemplative life at Mells, the ancient grey-stone Somersetshire manor-house filled with paintings by Frances Horner's pre-Raphaelite friends, where his family had lived since the Reformation. Katharine, serious and bookish, was very evidently his daughter, able to speak Greek more readily than she could make small talk to strangers. Diana Manners, her opposite in looks and personality, remembers them sampling Gunter's ices together in the 'Turkish' room at the Bath Club. Katharine's pale, beautiful face with its dark, arched eyebrows was grave as she 'explained literature and ethics . . . while I [Diana] sketched her a becoming dress for the next fancy ball'.

Cynthia Asquith, Raymond's sharp-tongued sister-in-law, professed shock at the cynicism of his friends, the Coterie. 'There is an insidiously corruptive poison in their midst, brilliantly distilled by their inspiration, Raymond.' Sibbie Hart-Davis, Duff Cooper's vivacious, highly-strung sister, was more admiring. Probably the Coterie and their high spirits gave her the outlet she craved from her claustrophobic marriage and priggish, penny-pinching husband. At any rate her recollection of the Coterie was of a 'society of brilliant and striking English personalities' with Diana Manners 'its centre and animator'. Through the summer Season of 1914, Sibbie left her husband at home while she attended Coterie parties where, according to her friend Nancy Cunard, 'one enjoyed oneself entirely, very much more than at the formal receptions and functions.' The

Coterie, in Duff Cooper's words, while 'very irritating to others' were 'utterly satisfying and delightful to themselves'.

It was John Manners, a distant cousin of Diana's, who first brought Duff into the Coterie. Until he met and made friends with John at Eton, Duff claimed to have known hardly anyone outside his immediate family and connections. The Manners' pre-war summer house-parties at Clovelly on the Devon coast – the house belonged to John's aunt and Lady Manners' sister, Mrs Hamlyn – unveiled a new and dazzling world to him. For six summers in succession including his Oxford vacations, he joined in the picnics, expeditions, midnight bathing-parties and charades; recited poetry and read aloud at after-dinner sessions in the drawing-room; took part in 'clandestine suppers in the kitchen amid whispers and laughter'. He was about to go for the seventh time in August 1914 when the war prevented it.

At Clovelly, as he noted in his autobiography, the guest-list invariably included, along with distinguished politicians and elderly men of letters, some of 'that brilliant company of young men, most of them slightly older than myself, who had already made a stir in the University of Oxford. They were almost famous and their sayings were quoted.' In this category Duff placed not only Raymond Asquith, Edward Horner, Billy and Julian Grenfell, but two more Old Etonians who had shared rooms with Edward and Julian at Oxford, two of the undergraduates Diana Manners had met during their reading-party in Norfolk. Their names were Charles Lister and Patrick Shaw-Stewart. Together these four friends had been elected to *Pop*, the elite society of Eton; together they went on to Balliol and together, although in different regiments on different fronts, they would take part in the Great War. Not one of them would return.

Already by summer 1914 they had set foot on very different paths. Shaw-Stewart, quick, able, socially ambitious, was anxious to make up for the lack of grandeur in his Scots military background. He was already making his mark in society, helped by his affair with Julian Grenfell's mother, Lady Desborough. Now, by recommending him to John Revelstoke of Baring's, the firm of City bankers, she took his career too under her wing. Despite her introduction, it was through sheer merit that Shaw-Stewart was made a partner while still in his mid-twenties. Nor did hard work cause his social life to suffer. A letter he wrote to Duff Cooper's sister Sybil from the trenches of Salonica in 1916, recalled this hectic socialising before the war. 'Since [Oxford],' he reminisced, 'as you very well know, Baring Bros, tennis, dining, dancing and love have usually taken up most of the time between 8 a.m. and 3.30 a.m. and left only a little surplus to bestow on sleep.' Patrick was not handsome – his photographs reveal a large-featured, bony face with a prominent nose – but he redeemed his lack of physical attraction with his cleverness, remarkable memory and sharp sense of humour. Julian Grenfell, suffering no doubt a twinge of filial jealousy, veered between loving and hating him. He liked his friend 'very much sometimes when he was a long way off and . . . liked being told the things he said'. But he found Patrick's love of money distasteful, along with his lack of 'the human-pity milk'.

Highly individualist, intolerant, politically conservative and an unabashed hedonist, Patrick Shaw-Stewart was much more part of the Coterie than the prickly, introverted Julian Grenfell, who was abroad in any case in 1914, soldiering in South Africa. The Grenfells (who became Desboroughs on their ennoblement) were a well-connected Buckinghamshire family, not in the first rank of aristocracy, nor as splendid as Etty Desborough's grandmother, the vastly rich Lady Cowper, might have wished for her granddaughter. But when Etty married Willy Grenfell in 1887, he was already the owner of Taplow Court, a large house high up on a hill near Maidenhead overlooking the Thames and surrounded by an estate of three thousand acres. Then in 1905, after he had sat in the Commons five years as a Conservative M.P., Willy was created first Earl Desborough by his friend, the outgoing Prime Minister, Arthur Balfour. Etty's inheritance of Panshanger in 1913 supplied the wealth to go with the title. The seat of the Cowpers, it was a vast pile, famed for its remarkable collection of pictures. In 1914 Etty sold a Raphael for £70,000 to pay for the installation of central heating.

Julian and Billy, the two older Grenfell sons, were tall and handsome, bright and athletic, this last natural enough in the children of a father who swam Niagara rapids and rowed alone across the Channel in an open boat. Now twenty-five, Billy had as an undergraduate played tennis and boxed for Oxford. Julian broke records show-jumping for his regiment in South Africa. At Balliol Billy excelled with an entrance exhibition and a first-class degree. With this profusion of gifts and with their family connections, the Grenfell brothers were natural members of the Manners–Asquith inner circle, but Diana Manners, for one, although admiring their physical qualities, remained cool about what she deemed a certain swaggering philistinism.

Charles Lister, a cheerful, ungainly eccentric, was much more immediately appealing. Despite being the son of Lord Ribblesdale, Lister had become a convinced socialist at Eton. He collected £75 'for the Russian people' in 1905 and each holiday returned to his parents' home at Gisburne where he kept a colony of rabbits, mice and guinea-pigs in the stables and subjected them to his own Utopian regime of diets and breeding-control. At Oxford he was a member of the Independent Labour Party and spent much time in Wimbledon campaigning with Betrand Russell for the suffragettes, or holding closeted meetings in his Balliol rooms where crowds of men gathered whom Julian Grenfell called 'the roughest . . . I have ever seen'. Charty Ribblesdale, Charles's fashionable socialite mother who was Margot Asquith's sister, was in despair, and approached the then Prime Minister Arthur Balfour for advice. He, according to Lister's gushing memorialist E. B. Osborn, 'took the common-sensible view of the matter, pointing out that the ILP intimacy would enable him to get all sorts of experience and a fund of special knowledge more valuable than that to be acquired by keeping a selling-plater [race-horse] or running a minor actress'. Lister took him at his word. Abandoning the rabbit colony, he took himself off (during a period of rustication from Oxford) to study the poor in the East End of London at close hand. Re-conversion followed, not immediately but swiftly enough for the critical Julian Grenfell to be disillusioned with such irresolution. 'I remember the time,' Charles Lister wrote before his death in 1915, 'when [Julian] was under the impression that I had chucked Socialism for the "loaves and fishes" etc. – and of course that sort of thing he couldn't abide. And he thought this for a longish while; then found out that it wasn't that after all, and took my hand in the most loving way . . .' In the meantime, Lister had joined the Diplomatic Corps, going first of all to Rome, where he was frustrated by the lack of responsibility he was given. ('I feel I'm looked on as a pleasant but sometimes rather tiresome child,' he wrote at the time.) On the eve of war he was in Constantinople from where, deeply pessimistic about the growing crisis in Europe, he predicted the advent of conflict long before any of his contemporaries were alive to the danger.

For the Coterie September 1913 in Venice, the last season there before the war, proved to be both a high water-mark and a finale. Diana Manners was there, staying under the wing of her mother in a house belonging to Lady Cunard in which the Prime Minister and Mrs Asquith were guests. Some distance away on the Grand Canal, Duff's friend George Vernon had taken a *palazzo* and filled it, Duff said, 'with nearly all the people whom I like best', the most 'precious' to Duff being Raymond Asquith and Charles Lister. Billy Grenfell also came. Sibbie Hart-Davis must have proved a trying member of the party. According to the letters which reached England, she seems to have mooned disconsolately about, playing the tragedy queen over her 'brisk, sensible' husband and dull marriage. Dennie Anson, who motored out with a party including Edward Horner, tried manfully to distract her with underwater swimming lessons.

The Coterie held canal races, played charades and, fortified by 'lashings of wine', stole kisses from each other on moonlit balconies. They travelled in gondolas to lavish parties and recited poetry aloud to the gondoliers who bore them home. The highlight of their stay was a 'wonderful fancy-dress ball' given by an Italian Marchesa who, while her guests danced the early hours away in the Piazza San Marco, appeared suddenly with 'very few clothes and a parrot on her shoulder, leading a leopard and followed by two black boys'. Entranced by such intimations of decadence, the Coterie vowed to return to Venice in 1914. But, says Diana Manners, this was their swansong, 'the Carne Vale . . . only Duff and I ever did return'.

But in the early summer of 1914 when Osbert Sitwell met Diana for the first time, her spirits were high and her horizons still unclouded. They met at Lady Cunard's house in Cavendish Square where Sir Thomas Beecham played *Der Rosenkavalier* to the guests after dinner. Sitwell, who admitted later to feeling shy, remembered her gratifying surprise at finding a Guards officer who could discuss Stravinsky. He himself, as many others had been, was amazed at her beauty, believing her to be 'the only classic of her kind and generation . . . The only beauty whose looks entitled her to be discussed by those who remembered the celebrated beauties of former days, the Comtesse de Castiglione, and Georgiana, Lady Dudley, debating whether she should have been half an inch taller or shorter . . .' Later on in the evening he accompanied her to a ball at a 'long tall brick house', ordinary outside, but inside frescoed with 'elephants and howdahs and rajahs and pavilions and melons and bulrushes in sepia and gold' by Sert. From all this spectacle, Sitwell's account of the evening centres round one incident, where a young girl leaning from the balcony dropped her glove. One of Diana's Coterie, Sir Denis Anson, immediately climbed down to retrieve it, dangling fearlessly from a drainpipe twenty feet above the ground.

Sitwell included this 'impetuous' escapade as characteristic of a daredevil who dived into the Thames and drowned after a night of revelry later on in the Season. But Anson's early death also afforded him the chance to reflect on the others who were soon to die young, not by their own mistakes, but because some Liberal statesmen presented a war to their sons for their coming-of-age. Sitwell himself would not be twenty-one until the month of December, but he remarks bitterly that, 'I attended . . . in 1914 many coming-of-age parties, when we toasted a future which was to have no substance . . . They stood, even at that moment, in the shadows . . .' His own coming-of-age was remarkable in retrospect only for his survival. 'I cannot think,' he says, 'of a single other host at such a party who outlasted the winter following.' This fact gives added significance to his memory of the 1914 Cavalry Ball at Knightsbridge Barracks, where Lord Kitchener sat holding court like a king in a bower of wreaths and flowers. To Sitwell, a survivor of the war into which Kitchener led the army, the general's face seemed 'tawny beyond sunburn and pertained to the planet Mars'.

Diana Manners too in her autobiography perceives an omen in a sudden death that summer – not that of Anson which took place in July, but the loss earlier of Gustav Hamel, the flying-ace. Hamel took off one June day from a French airfield, seen off by cheering crowds to fly to London. When he did not appear, his friends were reassured by newspaper reports that he was safe. Some of them even sailed to France, where they learnt the truth of his crash – presumably, since he was never found, over the Channel waters. Immediately in London dances were cancelled and Duff Cooper published an obituary poem in *The Times*. 'Hysterically upset' at the time, Diana Manners saw an added irony looking back on the tragedy afterwards. 'It was the first violent death,' she wrote, 'of a young man in my life.'

But in the June sunshine such thoughts seemed very far away to those who like the *Vanity Fair* cover-girl donned the new black and white motoring capes and took to the open road with young men in fast, shiny motors. To be windblown, to travel at speed in an open car (even when sheltering behind the obligatory goggles) was for the young a new and liberating sensation. 'The winds . . . were warm that summer,' recalled Osbert Sitwell, and the art – Steer, Sickert, Nicholson, Augustus John – on show in the newly-opened Chenil Gallery, a postage-stamp-sized room near the Post Office in Chelsea's King's Road, reflected this. 'Young women . . . crowned with large straw hats,' remembered Sitwell, 'lounging wistfully . . . in undulating . . . landscapes – with the feel of sea and mountain in the air round them.'

The dashing young men driving girls in open motor-cars were christened in 1914 parlance, the 'Nuts'. A generation before they had been 'Dudes' or 'Stage-door Johnnies', and no respectable girl would have entered a carriage with them unchaperoned. The 'Nuts' took their name from a revue which had recently opened at the Palace Theatre, *The Passing Show*. A roaring success, it made an idol of Basil Hallam, its twenty-five-year-old star. Moustached and languidly elegant, he strutted on stage in a grey top-hat and morning-coat, and made his number into the hit of the show:

> I'm Gilbert the Filbert, the Nut with a K,
> The Pride of Piccadilly, the blasé roué.
> Oh, Hades, the ladies all leave their wooden huts
> For Gilbert the Filbert, the Colonel of the Nuts.

A year later, while still at the height of his popularity, Basil Hallam joined the Royal Flying Corps and went to France. One year later still he was dead, shot down in a balloon flying over enemy lines. But his song remained – to many of his generation inextricably linked with that last summer before the war, when young men fresh from visiting their tailors in Savile Row or Jermyn Street, would tell each other, 'What a K-nut you look!'

London, the centre of the empire, was according to Osbert Sitwell, a city designed for men. It catered to his needs from the moment when every morning he left his Wellington Barracks quarters to be given a shave and hairbrush by the famous G. F. Trumper, hairdresser to George V. The London clubs and the shops – Lock's the hatters, Berry's the wine merchants, Sotheran's for old books and Fores for sporting pictures – had a solid, comfortable, masculine air. London was the mecca for leather goods and men's tailoring. It was to Paris that women went for female fripperies and high-fashion clothes. Each night, dressed in white tie and tails, with white kid gloves, carrying a gold-topped cane and sporting a white gardenia, Osbert Sitwell would walk miles back from some dance or supper-party to the barracks through the streets of London. There, from his room on the second floor overlooking St James's Park and Buckingham Palace, shrouded in canvas and scaffolding, he could watch 'thousands of lights . . . as far as you could see'. He could feel at the very heart and centre of the city, 'with access to every pleasure, every mystery, every whisper, of the town'. Diana Manners, by contrast, at twenty years of age, could not walk, drive, shop or even travel by taxi through London alone. Hotels were similarly forbidden to her, apart from the Ritz. Pearl Barrington Crake was not allowed to go out tête-à-tête if invited. 'The young men could only come and fetch you to take you on to a dinner party. My mother said, "You've got to pretend to pay for the taxi," but of course the men always paid.' Certainly, she never sampled the illicit delights of a nightclub like the basement Cabaret Club in Beak Street, where 'in the small hours . . . the rhythm of the primitive forms of ragtime' bounced off Wyndham Lewis's Vorticist-frescoed walls.

Ragtime had exploded into London's West End in 1912, when a revue called *Hullo Rag-time!* had opened on Christmas Eve at the London Hippodrome. 'It was as if,' wrote J. B. Priestley when he discovered ragtime, 'we had been still living in the nineteenth century and then suddenly found the twentieth glaring and scream-ing at us. We were yanked into our own age, fascinating, jungle-haunted, monstrous. We were used to being sung at in music halls in a robust and zestful fashion, but the syncopated frenzy of these . . . Americans was something quite different. . .' American singing star Ethel Levy belted out the brassy, strident ragtime music; Shirley Kellogg danced the chorus-girls along a raised walkway at right angles to the stage. The show ran in all for 451 performances, and for ten of these Rupert Brooke was in the audience. As a result of *Hullo Rag-time!* negro dance-bands became fashionable from the suburbs to Mayfair and Belgravia, and Scheherazade skirts could be seen incongruously swaying and dipping to their uninhibited rhythms. 'I can't tell you how glad I am the Season is over,' wrote Edward Marsh after two months of this, in July 1913. 'It got bloodier and bloodier – the onestep – turkeytrot – bunnyhug or fishwalk or whatever you choose to call it – carried all before it, and my general dislike of its vulgarity, combined with my particular dislike of being on the shelf as a nontrotter – hugger or walker, worked me up into a fine frenzy of disgust and socialism . . . A few more such evenings and I shall have no noble and picturesque Toryism left for you to explain away. The negrification of Society will soon be complete – and black faces will be an essential part of evening dress.'

The Passing Show was theatreland's outstanding success in 1914, but many other plays displayed a healthy box-office. At the Vaudeville *The Dangerous Age*, a 'modern' comedy, dared to enact a forty-year-old woman's love for a twenty-two-year-old youth. The reviewers, while not openly disapproving, took care to poke fun at the 'love-lorn matron' and applauded heartily her eventual decision to do the decent thing by marrying a man twice her age. Wilde's *An Ideal Husband* had been revived as a vehicle for Phyllis Nielson, Ellen Terry's daughter. At the Prince of Wales Lady Randolph Churchill's play *The Bill* was enthusiastically received – by her friends if not by the critics. *Pygmalion* shocked theatre-goers even before the curtain rose, by including the word 'bloody' in advertisements outside the theatre. At the Aldwych Chekov's *Uncle Vanya* was described as 'a very strange play'. In May Dame Nellie Melba had sung in *Tosca*, a gala for the royal Danish visit. She returned to Covent Garden in June to sing Desdemona in *Otello*, and for one glorious gala to take part with Caruso in *La Bohème*. A new scheme, the People's Theatre Society, devised in 1914 by Sir Herbert Tree and Mrs Patrick Campbell, enabled the less well-off to buy cheap seats for 3d each. For *Pygmalion* on Sunday evenings, a working-class audience was let in free. For all its good intentions, the People's Theatre Society had to contend with strong competition from the new 'bioscopes' such as the one in Kingsway, showing *Harry Lauder Among the Mormons*. At the White City, still one of London's remaining pleasure-gardens now that Vauxhall had vanished, the Anglo-American Exposition tempted Londoners with 'America's Sky-Scrapers – The Grand Canyon – Wonders of the Panama Canal'.

Meanwhile, the fashionable took up the habit of dining on Sunday nights at one of the many new and already highly successful grill-rooms in London's best hotels. '*Les dîners amusants*,' commented the *Standard*, trying to conjure for its readers 'the characteristic Parisian atmosphere' of these evenings. Indeed, one of the most popular haunts was the Berkeley's own Parisian Café, designed by Lutyens in a 'late Renaissance' style in heliotrope and white; or the cream-coloured Savoy Restaurant; or else the light, mirrored Carlton, where Escoffier reigned still as *chef de cuisine*. 'Drive *like hell* to the Ritz,' Sybil Hart-Davis would say getting into a taxi at the Berkeley exactly opposite and, deposited by a perfect U-turn at its door, would lunch in the Louis XVI restaurant amidst statuary and cream marble columns. In the evenings the daring danced in nightclubs – the Lotus, Murray's, the Four Hundred – cooling themselves down with gin fizzes, mint juleps and cherry flips as 'a small negro band . . . hoot[ed] itself hoarse with whip-poor-will chuckles . . .' Or else, Osbert Sitwell continued with his reminiscence, he would go to the Alhambra with his Brigade of Guards cronies to admire 'the serried ranks of beauties on the stage, the curls and legs and eyes in line'.

For young bachelors like these, the Cavendish Hotel in Jermyn Street provided a sort of adult nursery, where they could over-indulge in champagne and sow wild oats with impunity under the watchful eye of Rosa Lewis, its châteleine. At forty-seven Rosa Lewis was still the superb cook she had been in the Edwardian era, when her skill had taken her from obscure kitchen maid to friend and equal of Society, and even an acquaintanceship with the King. In 1907 the Kaiser himself had invited her aboard his yacht, as a guest not a cook. As a result his signed photograph was displayed prominently in the Cavendish kitchens, until August 4 when it was summarily taken down.

Rosa's insistence was always for simple methods and fresh ingredients. 'Englishwomen should give [the grill] pride of place in their kitchens,' was her advice in the recipe column she wrote for the *Daily Mail*. In her own hotel she bought and even killed herself the turtles required for her celebrated turtle soup.

The Cavendish, lined with panelling and furnished with wing chairs and comfortable sofas, had the welcoming air of a private country house. Rosa, rich on £6000 per season solely from her flourishing catering business (dinners cooked by her 'girls' were delivered by bus to as many as five or six hostesses a night) could afford to treat her guests like friends. As friends they made up their own bills, and those who could afford to pay did. In return, generals and colonels could be seen dining quite contentedly in the Cavendish's pantry, while officers' wives helped the staff with breakfast. Meanwhile, Rosa gave famous parties costing several hundred pounds for 'Nuts' and Gaiety girls, and in her old-fashioned

Edwardian costumes, presided benevolently but strictly over both food and guests alike.

The style of the Cavendish was racy but – just – respectable. In 1914 among those staying there was Sir William Eden, Anthony Eden's father, who used the Cavendish annexe in Duke Street as his London retreat. Although his permanent home was not the Cavendish but Windlestone in Yorkshire, he persuaded Rosa to 'improve' the annexe by knocking down the dividing wall between it and the hotel. An art-lover and exhibiting painter, Sir William was also at heart a reactionary and short-tempered English squire. He loathed dogs, despised the colour red, hated children and kept up a constant flow of grumbles to Rosa about dust and noise. Typical of his complaints was the letter written to her on May 25 1914:

> 'Dear Madam,
>   I am sorry to complain and needs must when the devil drives, and you are the devil whilst you are amusing yourself which is all you do with your lovers, your dogs, your cocktails and your caterwauling . . .'

However, he also corresponded with her when he was away, writing to say how much he missed her cooking, and she could console herself with the observation that he treated his wife in much the same quarrelsome manner. Sir William bickered too with George Moore, Sickert, Shackleton and other friends who came to the Cavendish to visit him. His tantrums invariably ran their course in full view of every guest in the hotel. Lord Ribblesdale, another eccentric resident, meanwhile distributed clothes, charity and carriage-rides to penniless children he spied outside in the streets.

To them all, whether old Society or new (politicians, newspaper proprietors, actors, impresarios and authors all patronised her hotel), Rosa Lewis dispensed hospitality and her individual brand of brisk but tolerant humour. 'I enjoyed every hour,' she said later of her life, 'up to 1914.'

Since the 1880's the Café Royal in Regent Street with its gilded walls and unlikely decor of cherubs and caryatids, had been the principal haunt of London's literary and artistic circles. By 1914 sightseers, loud-voiced subalterns and impressionable suburban bank-clerks almost outnumbered the bohemian creative spirits they had come to see. As a result the back entrance of the Café was a mecca for bookmakers, touts, moneylenders and conmen, preying on the naive or the unwary. But you could still buy paintings 'under the table' from penniless Chelsea Set models or artists with too many meals already 'on the slate'. The Café, despite its rock-bottom prices, gave credit freely and generously; its waiters even lent money at ten shillings 'danger' interest. Auguste Judah, the lanky, distinguished manager, allowed his clients to sit from opening to closing time over a beer and a six-penny plate of chips.

When Augustus John, capaciously cloaked, appeared with his long flowing locks and golden ear-rings, the Slade students playing dominoes or chess with matchsticks would stand eagerly to attention. John sat invariably by himself, broodingly nursing his whisky-soda; if, as sometimes happened, he dozed, his fellow-artists respectfully lowered their voices. Jacob Epstein frequented the Café; so did the young Gaudier-Brzeska, recognisable to the talent-spotters by his trademark of blue workman's shirts. The artist Adrian Allinson arrived by motorbike, incongruously clad for the journey in velvet coat with an outsize black stock. Ashley Dukes, one of the 'New Agers', brought in Rupert Brooke occasionally. More often he arrived with his flat-mate, the mathematician and philosopher T. E. Hulme.

New Age was one of the many flourishing small Georgian magazines. *Blast*, the mouthpiece of Vorticism, was another, launched by the fiery, pugnacious Wyndham Lewis and bringing to England, so he thought, its very own brand of Futurism – 'The English Parallel Movement to Cubism and Expressionism ... Deathblow to Impressionism'. From the Omega Workshop – founded in Fitzroy Square by Roger Fry – Wyndham Lewis and C. R. Nevinson, son of the famous correspondent, seceded to their own Rebel Art Centre in Great Ormond Street. The flat of Lechmere, its director, was a temple to Futurism with black curtains and black-painted doors. He boasted of commissioning a Cubist rock-garden with 'strange, stunted trees from Japan'. Meanwhile at Omega, Roger Fry continued to try to introduce a spirit of twentieth-century fun into the manufacture of tables, carpets, fabrics and chairs. His pride and joy was a 'conversational chair' with vivid blue and yellow legs and a round blue and green seat. It was witty enough, Fry told a newspaperman, for even Max Beerbohm to sit on. 'Fry,' wrote Brooke after visiting Omega during the summer of 1914, 'I found ... as plausible and delightful as ever. Almost he persuaded me to be a – whatever the latest thing is – Paroxist, I believe. I went over the . . . Workshops: but I could see little except the animals, lampshades and rugs that pleased me. I thought the chairs and the cushions *too* shoddy.' Nevertheless, by that summer Omega at last was flourishing. Fry could afford to pay his artists thirty shillings a week. Brezska, who was one of them, had sold several drawings. A commission for stained-glass windows and another for a mosaic floor had filled the order-book. French and German manufacturers were interested. The enthusiasm for things Russian had stimulated a desire for new decorative patterns and exotic colour combinations. At last, Fry thought, there was a chance to become 'a little civilised' even in what he called this 'Bird's Custard Island'. 'Civilisation and a desire for the things of the spirit,' Virginia Woolf echoed in her essay on Fry, 'seemed to be taking hold not merely of a small group, but to be breaking through among the poor, among the rich . . .'

To Mark Hayler and his family, spiritual pursuits were nothing new. Nor was the idealism with which they tried to spread their religion, their outlook, their certainty to those who had either never had it or had lost it along life's way. On June 13 March Hayler and his father saw the Prince of Wales visit the Salvation Army in Kennington. 'We stood on the Crimean Monument in Waterloo Place to see the Army procession march to Hyde Park.' Together father and son campaigned against the sale of liquor in theatres. They were joined by the unlikely figure of Mrs Ormiston, a suffragette who wrote hymns. The Lewisham meetings of the Esperanto Society; the Children's Welfare Exhibition at Olympia; Sunday services at Whitfield's Tabernacle – Mark Hayler's days so far that summer had been long, full and happy. At night with other young men, he tramped the length of the Thames Embankment, giving fatherly exhortations and breakfast vouchers to the sleeping tramps. 'If I didn't go out I read – Galsworthy's *Justice* – or wrote to T. P. O'Connor's *Great Thoughts*, a weekly literary paper. I even had two articles published in the local paper on the theme of "The safety of the people is the highest law", an ironic theme considering what was just about to land on us.'

Diana Manners' hopes for the new age were no less fervent but rather more worldly. 'There was a general new look in everything,' she claimed later, 'in those last years before the first war – a Poiret-Bakst blazon and a budding freedom of behaviour that was breaking out at the long last end of Victorianism.'

To Osbert Sitwell too the future seemed enticing: 'All classes

[79]

still believed in absolute progress . . . How far distant did we stand, it seemed, from the brutalities of the Georgian Age and of the early Victorian . . .' But mixed with the excitement was a restlessness. His friends were restive – planning trips to China, ranches in South America, a polar expedition, a commission in an African regiment. It was, he felt, as if some strange kind of disturbance had come upon them, like animals and birds before an earthquake or before the eruption of a volcano. Even the new music reflected this, according to J. B. Priestley. Out of ragtime, for example, came 'fragmentary but prophetic outlines' of the threat to the emerging century – 'the menace to old Europe, the domination of America, the emergence of Africa, the end of confidence and any feeling of security . . . the frenzy, the underlying despair' of our age, most of which would come to the fore with the First Great War.

In the more sedate circles of the Court, a threat to the Season was distinguished in the new fashion of dining out. 'No more dinner parties for twenty,' mourned *Vanity Fair*. 'Now we dine in quartettes at a smart restaurant off four courses, and then on to a music-hall . . . Society has grown lax, and Society nowadays finds as much amusement in long weekends out of town and early flittings to country and Continent as in the stereotyped programme in town.' For the 1914 Season, families no longer took a Mayfair house: a cupboard-sized flat or even an hotel bedroom sufficed. From mid-June Hyde Park grew emptier as earlier each year, it seemed, Society scattered. 'We are watching,' *Vanity Fair* was convinced in 1914, 'the gradual waning of the Season.'

Only the Queen seemed determined 'to get Society back into its good habit of remaining on in town until the end-proper of the Season – that once all-important Friday before Goodwood . . .' The Queen's wishes were reinforced in 1914 by the enforced postponement of the June 29 Court Ball. It was put off until July while the Court mourned the events at Sarajevo.

'They shot the Archduke, didn't they?' says Hilda French. 'At the time I didn't think much of it.' Harold Macmillan, an Oxford undergraduate, was coming out of a Commemoration Ball when he saw the words on a bill-board: Archduke assassinated. A Slav nationalist had shot the heir to the Austro–Hungarian throne. 'The murder,' wrote Herbert Asquith, son of the Prime Minister, 'roused horror and disgust in every corner of the globe. But it was some time before it was realized by the public that a lever had been suddenly pressed over in the vast structure of check and balances which preserved the peace of Europe, and that once that lever was pulled, the machinery of war would go relentlessly to work.' 'We never thought the Kaiser would do it in the end,' is Mark Hayler's view. 'After all, he was a relative of Queen Victoria. The Queen died practically in the Kaiser's arms. He was at her bedside. But he was a vain, foolish man, more foolish than we knew.

'We were friends with Germany,' he continues. 'The very time the Archduke was shot, one hundred parsons came over from Germany to a meeting I went to in the City Temple. They came to the centre of the League of Progressive Thought, under the auspices of R. J. Campbell, author of *The New Theology*. Even there, in that place, there were rumblings of war. Yet, when it actually happened, the English weren't prepared for it. They took the outbreak of war far too philosophically. They didn't fight against it soon enough or strongly enough. They remembered the Boer War and thought it would make very little difference to their lives. After all, *they* weren't within enemy range.'

Ironically, the news of the shooting of the Archduke came through during Kiel Yachting Week when two squadrons of the British Fleet lay anchored in German waters. As the great ships of both nations moored fraternally side by side, the Kaiser donned a British Admiral's uniform and was cheered by British sailors. The officers staged daytime regattas and in the evenings toasted each other at shipboard banquets. It was a shining display of peace and friendship, according to William Goodenough, captain of one of the cruisers present, *HMS Southampton*. At a dinner on board his vessel a German officer gave a toast during which he was heard to declare, 'War between us would be like civil war.'

On June 28, within an hour of the news of the assassination reaching Kiel, the ceremony and festivities came abruptly to an end. The Kaiser, plunged into mourning both political and personal for his friend Archduke Ferdinand, made a solitary and dramatic journey shorewards from his racing yacht *Hohenzollern*. That same evening he left Kiel for his capital, Berlin. Quietly the British Fleet too slipped anchor and set course for home.

In London the excited newsboys shouting 'King of Orstria murdered!' brought back memories to one young Territorial Force soldier of the six months he had recently spent in Germany. Studying in Berlin, Lance Corporal H. G. R. Williams had got to know a Lieutenant in a Saxon *Jaeger* regiment. 'We openly discussed the possibility of war. We discussed taking each other prisoner. That was why I joined the TA. I saw trouble coming and felt it was up to me to do something about it.'

Still, though 'war was on the cards', there was no thought on this late June weekend that it was literally round the corner. To Lance Corporal Williams the TA was still 'a club', very much 'the thing to do. It had good social and sporting facilities.' His own thoughts about it and about the summer ahead were distinctly unmilitary. 'The TA camp was coming up – this year at Birling Gap on Beachy Head. I looked forward to Eastbourne, to bathing in the sea, to getting away from London.'

Diana Manners was spending the last weekend of June staying at Robertsbridge with the Trees. There were not enough beds, she recalls, and so the contingent of young feasted and danced the night away. At dawn they drove to Battle Abbey, then breakfasted at Bodiam Castle. They returned that Sunday morning to find the papers full of the assassination. It seemed, Diana Manners thought, a remote event which could not possibly affect them. Despite the apprehensions voiced by their older and wiser host, Sir Herbert Tree, the young people 'fell upon the hard daisied grass and slept the sleep of happy ignorance'.

4

July

TEN DAYS AFTER the assassination at Sarajevo, Osbert Sitwell recalls Basil Zaharoff, the arms-dealer, being pointed out to him at a London luncheon. 'There must be something up,' the friend accompanying Sitwell is supposed to have remarked prophetically, 'or he wouldn't be here! His arrival is always a sign of trouble, and every European Chancellor makes a point of knowing where he is.' Then, warming to his theme of predestined disaster, Sitwell warns that by July 1914, 'already in every capital, the birds of prey were assembling, hovering, watching; the politicians would supply the carrion, though not in their own person.'

It was the innocent young, in Sitwell's view, who were to provide the carrion. On their unsuspecting heads, claimed Harold Macmillan, the war dropped 'as a bolt from the blue'. 'A few experts feared the Germans,' was his view of the events of 1914. 'Ordinary people didn't which made it all the more traumatic.' Christopher Isherwood found proof of this on reading his mother's 1914 diary: 'A document which records without the dishonesty of hindsight, the day-to-day approach to a catastrophe by an utterly unsuspecting victim.'

Yet to us, looking back, the atmosphere of the period up to 1914 seems loud with the murmurings of an approaching conflict. Looking back on the growing sense of rivalry between the two great powers – commercial, political and increasingly military – and the paranoia and hostility this engendered, it seems hard to imagine that war in Europe, when it came, could have been regarded as anything other than the climax of an ineluctable process. For years talk of war with Germany had been in the air. Evelyn Waugh, an eleven-year-old schoolboy dreaming of his future not as a writer but as an artist, drew pictures of 'German cavalry plunging among English infantry with much blood and gunpowder about'. With his London schoolfellows he played war games, brandishing an old pistol on derelict land. Their play – digging a redoubt and stocking it with tinned food for an emergency – reflected their belief that the German invaders were coming. 'The theme must have been much in the air,' Waugh reflected later, while his brother Alec's reaction was to blame all this pre-1914 warmongering on the imperialism, insularity and 'top-dog' mentality instilled in the English at their public schools.

Eric Linklater, whose autobiography *Fanfare for a Tin Hat* recalls his repeated, thwarted efforts to enlist on the outbreak of war as a scrawny, short-sighted fifteen-year-old, likened the patriotism of his age to modern protest movements. 'Protest,' he claimed, 'is regarded as a contemporary phenomenon. But in 1914 protest was louder, more general and much angrier than it is today. It was, however, all directed against the insufferable pretensions of the German Empire and the brutal behaviour of its marching armies. Indignation was fierce and popular . . .'

For the country which traditionally ruled the waves the Kaiser's ship-building drive, directly challenging British naval supremacy on the high seas, was especially hard to accommodate. From 1907 onwards xenophobia mounted and fears of a German invasion grew. 'We want eight and we won't wait' ran a popular line of doggerel, demanding additional battleships for the Royal Navy. Music-hall songs and popular orators like the socialist and Germanophobe Robert Blatchford swelled the chorus. In 1908 and 1909 a spy scare sent elderly Tories scurrying to put pen to print in the *Daily Telegraph*. A Major Reed from Perthshire denounced 1500 traitors in the pay of the German General Staff at large in industrial Scotland. Henry James, made nervous in 1909 by all the talk of invasion, wrote from his house at Rye only half-jokingly to a friend: 'When the German Emperor carries the next war into this country, my chimney-pots, visible to a certain distance out at sea, may be his very first objective . . .'

'Be Prepared!' was the motto of the Boy Scouts founded in 1908 by the hero of Mafeking, Lieutenant-General Sir Robert Baden-Powell, and boasting by 1910 100,000 members. 'To the Day! The anticipated German invasion of 1913 . . .' screamed the headlines of an inflammatory advertisement toasting Hall's Wine Tonic in the British press. This, it boomed, was 'the toast that is drunk nightly at every mess on every battleship . . . of the German Navy . . . [It] means the time when the Fatherland finds herself strong enough to strike out for the World Empire which we possess . . . We cannot all be sailors or soldiers,' it continued, 'but we can all keep fit' in readiness. Hall's Wine Tonic would perform this service, enabling lusty British manhood to do its part on 'The Day'.

Others, notably Earl Roberts, Commander-in-Chief during the Boer War, put their trust in compulsory military service, rather than in any potion offered by Messrs Hall. A 1906 tract in favour of conscription cited the need for a 'clarion call . . . which shall inspire us to march forward . . .' Anthony Eden, a teenage Eton schoolboy with an older brother studying in Germany (Timothy Eden who was later interned there) remembers frequent family discussions about Lord Roberts' military service campaign.

Much of the press, typified by the *Daily Mail* and the rest of the Northcliffe empire, used the scare of a German invasion to fill pages and sell copies to their indignant readership. Robert Blatchford prophesied doom regularly in the pages of the *Weekly Dispatch*, pinpointing Holland and Belgium as the sparks which would touch off the flame of European war. The weekly *John Bull* was rabidly anti-German. Novelists and playwrights even took up the theme. Anthony Eden was among the packed audiences who flocked to see Charles Doughty's *An Englishman's Home*, in which Germans thinly disguised as 'foreigners' raided a middle-class Essex house. The owner, a bonhomous golfer who disliked arms and shirked his duty in the Territorial Force, was ill-prepared and paid dearly for such carelessness. Erskine Childers' *The Riddle of the Sands*; 'Saki' Munro's *When William Came*; P. G. Wodehouse's *The Snoop* (in which Boy Scouts foiled an attempted landing): the 'invasion' novels followed fast and fashionable. Children inevitably absorbed the anti-German mood of the country. A prize-winning schoolboy poem two or three years before the war warned:

> England, narrow seas divide thee
>   From the foe
> Guard the waves lest ill betide thee;
> Lest the foe that lurks beside thee
>   Lay thee low.

By July 1914, it seems true to say, the notion of war, war with Germany, far from being a bolt from the blue, had virtually become commonplace. Its declaration in August, if not actually anticipated, might have been expected to arouse little surprise. Indeed, already in

[85]

1912 Julian Grenfell had written matter-of-factly home from South Africa: 'I suppose we aren't going to fight the Germans yet from what Haldane told you.'

But simply because the idea of European war had been discussed for so long, now when the crisis was finally approaching, its impact was dulled, its true significance dangerously underestimated. The *Manchester Guardian* spoke for many when at last in the closing week of July, it warned of the approach of 'the European war which has been talked about for so long that no one really believed it would ever come . . .'

Throughout July the British Government, and Asquith in particular, seemed preoccupied with the Irish question. Over the assassination of the Archduke, Asquith himself had shown little concern. Dismissing it in his diary as an internal crisis for the German and Austro-Hungarian empire to deal with, he saw no reason why 'we should be anything more than spectators'. Twice at least before 1914 a crisis had been averted, and the Great Powers had managed to avoid entanglement in the localised Balkan Wars. It had been a difficult achievement. The constantly feuding Balkan peninsula was like a tinder-box ready to spark, with Russia greedy for Mediterranean expansion at the expense of her weakened neighbour, Turkey; and Austria, nervous of the Slavs under her control, determined to prevent this, with the support of Germany. But because conflict had been avoided in the dangerous circumstances of 1908 and 1912, there seemed no reason to suppose that peace, if it was threatened, could not be maintained through diplomatic negotiation again and again. On January 1 1914 the British Chancellor of the Exchequer, Lloyd George, had claimed confidently that the prospects for world peace had never been so bright. 'Never has the sky been more perfectly blue.' His colleague, Sir Edward Grey, had welcomed 1914, 'a year of rejoicing for peace'. An Anglo-American Peace League had already been formed to honour this prospect. Even Winston Churchill, reassured by the apparent tranquillity of the spring and early summer of 1914, had thought the time ripe to begin thinking about naval deceleration. Germany had slowed down her rate of shipbuilding since 1912. In any case, he recalled in *The World Crisis* published in 1922, 'There had been a score of opportunities had any power wished to make war.' Lady Ottoline Morrell, on a visit to Asquith at his country home, the Wharf, on July 25, was reassured even at this late stage by his nonchalant attitude. 'I went a walk with Asquith along the river and into the meadows,' she wrote in her diary. 'I asked him what would happen about Austria and Serbia. He said with a laugh – "This will take the attention away from Ulster, which is a good thing." He did not seem worried.'

Alec Waugh, looking forward to a summer holiday away from his detested school, remembers 'no clouds on my horizon during those long July evenings . . . when the Chief [Headmaster] in his farewell speech spoke of the bad news in the morning papers, I thought he was referring to the civil war in Ireland.' Christopher Isherwood's mother, writing in her diary on July 13, noted apprehensively that, 'The papers look fearfully serious . . . Ulster is an armed camp . . . Sir Edward Grey says, "if it be not peace with honour, it must be war with honour."' The rhetoric was uncannily that of the First World War, but Grey was referring not to Germany but to Ulster.

Links between England and Germany were historically and personally close. Already Prince Henry of Prussia, the Kaiser's brother, had informed his cousin, King George, that he would be attending the yachting in July at Cowes. The Prime Minister of Britain was only one of many fathers to entrust his children to the care of a German governess. Later, when these children grew up, they might have expected to attend a German university before going on to an English college. The war poet, Charles Sorley, was one of many young men before the war who did so. Having left Marlborough at Christmas 1913, he spent the spring and summer of 1914 in Germany. He was on a walking tour along the banks of the Moselle during July and the first days of August. With a friend he was arrested at Trier and jailed for one day before being asked to leave the country. Nevertheless, 'I regard the war as one between sisters,' he could say at its beginning. '. . . The German nature is the nicest in the world, as far as it is not warped by the German Empire.'

There was in many quarters of the country a deep-rooted belief that war between two civilized, industrialized twentieth-century nations, interdependent on each other in trade and finance was, when it came to it, impossible. Wall Street and Threadneedle Street would prevent it, reasoned George Winterbourne, the hero of Richard Aldington's novel *Death of a Hero*. 'Between them [they] could stop the universe.' They could certainly halt this puny war. Kenneth Clark, an eleven-year-old schoolboy holidaying with his family at Loch Ewe in Scotland, spent August 2 in the relaxed company of the Governor of the Bank of England. 'There's talk of war,' said Lord Cunliffe over lunch on board Kenneth Clark Senior's yacht. 'It will never happen; the Germans haven't got the credits.' Young Kenneth who remembers being much impressed, wondered idly why at such a crisis the Governor had not returned to London. But it was August: 'That would have been unthinkable.'

Despite all the talk, the reality of a Great War actually occurring in 1914 was equally unthinkable. 'It is almost unbelievable,' wrote a contemporary in July, 'that Europe is going to fight over a place like Serbia.' The Archduke was personally unpopular. The Serbs were not only far off, but backward and disreputable. The Cambridge don A. C. Benson was one of many who shrugged off the assassination as unimportant. 'He was a curious, dumb, reserved, uncomfortable sort of man,' was his curt epitaph for the dead Archduke. Meanwhile, with the summer vacation in progress, he had more important events to record in his diary. 'Rupert Brooke came to dine –' ended that day's entry; 'very handsome but more mature since his travels'.

The 1914 generation of British children, said Churchill, was taught from the safe and secure viewpoint of their prosperous age, 'of the Great War against Napoleon as the culminating effort in the history of the British peoples ... They looked on Waterloo and Trafalgar as the supreme achievement of British arms ...' For forty-three years up to 1914 there had been peace in Europe. France harboured bitter memories still of the Franco–Prussian conflict and the ignominious rout of the French army in 1871, but in England there had been no great war to disturb the march of progress and prosperity since Wellington rode victorious from the field of Waterloo. 'We are in the trough of peace that had lasted a hundred years between two great conflicts,' wrote Osbert Sitwell, summing up his parents' age and his own pre-war era. 'In it such wars as arose were not general, but only a brief armed version of the Olympic Games. You won a round; the enemy won the next. There was no more talk of extermination, or of Fights to a Finish, than would occur in a boxing match.' The Great War of 1914 finally turned around the belief in progress, the meliorist creed with which the average Englishman had held faith for the century since 1815. The events which hinged on the coming war were to change the outlook of a nation. But until then their belief in the inexorable march of progress and the inevitable triumph of civilisation remained innocently intact.

And so, *Vanity Fair* noted in early July, 'Beyond the postponement of the Court Ball and the week of Court mourning, the lamented deaths of the Archduke Ferdinand and his charming wife affected but little the ordinary social round in [London].' July 4, Independence Day, brought the usual fireworks displays and dances among the American community. Ninety Civil War veterans visited the Anglo-American Exposition and watched a game of baseball at Shepherd's Bush. The youngest of them was in his seventies: the oldest, a venerable 105. In the evening the American Ambassador was among the crowds of celebrants at a Savoy 'Carnival', at which bouquets tied in red and blue ribbons were distributed to the guests.

Meanwhile, the sale of modern art by Christies drew crowds to Bond Street to watch the hammer fall on a Corot for the record price of almost £7000. At an early July reunion dinner of the Cambridge University Liberal Club, a suffragette emerged from underneath the table to harangue the astonished members. How dare they feast while women in prison fasted? On July 6 the Harvard Club of London gave dinner at the Savoy to all Harvard men in England in honour of the crews who had come from Cambridge, Massachusetts to row at Henley. Americans, almost fifty thousand of them the *Daily Mirror* estimated, had filled the London hotels, where they gave private dinner parties to repay their English hosts. American women in what the *Mirror* noted had become their summer uniform ('white canvas boots, suits of fine blue serge, straw hats') thronged the shopping streets and set their electric fans whizzing in American strongholds like the riverside Hotel Cecil, whose Palm Court had become 'the rendezvous of Americans in London'. The July heat wave brought queues of customers to the new American soda-fountain in the Strand, while further up the street at the Savoy, staff pressed buttons to open their sliding plate-glass windows and catch any cooling river breezes from the Thames.

The 'grilling hot' July days succeeded one another. Siegfried Sassoon, who had forsaken Weirleigh, his mother's country home in Kent for the urban life and 'an enterprising existence which would give me something to write about', sweltered in the London streets. In his rented rooms in Theobalds Road, found for him by Eddie Marsh, he could visualize the Kentish summer: 'The Weald . . . in its green contentedness'; the leafy apple orchards; the tennis court; the long, light days spent playing cricket. Yet for all the appeal of this pleasant, pastoral life, Sassoon by 1914 had felt compelled to leave it. For the past year or so he had felt himself stagnating mentally. 'I had absolutely nothing to look forward to after the hunting season except playing cricket . . .' Since Cambridge seven years earlier, Sassoon's achievements had been conspicuous by their absence. His overdraft, on the other hand, was noteworthy and with four hunters in the field each winter, likely to become even more so. In May 1914 Sassoon decided it was time to shake himself out of his torpor. 'Blast the money! What I want is to get out of my groove.'

His plan was to shut himself away in his London rooms and write every morning at a table on which stood his Oxford dictionary and a pristine sheet of blotting-paper. In the afternoons, he would edify himself with visits to museums and galleries. Such was the plan. In reality, of course, Sassoon was far too undisciplined to keep even to this untaxing schedule. At Cambridge, having changed his subject from law to history, he had left – as, he consoled himself, Tennyson did – without a degree. Nevertheless, his mother, proud of her son's literary pretensions, encouraged his plans to live on his £500 a year private income and write high-minded books of Tennysonian verse which he could afford to have published privately. At Weirleigh, Sassoon had an ideal studio in which to write, a lofty 'book-room' looking out over a terraced English garden, with roses spilling over arches and white pigeons cooing in a loft. But only nine slim volumes of 'unsatisfactory sonnets' had appeared under the imprint of the Athenaeum Press between the time he was nineteen and twenty-six.

Now, in London in July 1914, Sassoon's days began to be 'more and more a matter of going out and trying not to feel at a loose end'. He had a propensity to board London buses on impulse, and then stay on them to see where they went – invariably a far-flung destination like Kew Gardens or Hornsey Rise, which ensured a long and time-consuming journey back to the city centre again. Further hours spent ensconced in a comfortable armchair at his club, dozing over their papers or their editions of poetry and *belles-lettres*, were 'just enough to make me feel that I'd got something to do'. But as the days wore on, Sassoon grew increasingly moody and depressed. So lonely was he that he looked forward to his few engagements for days ahead; and so impecunious that his four horses finally had to be sold – one of them, ironically, to a Belgian cavalry officer who intended, in these days of peace, to use it for show-jumping. Sassoon's outings to the opera or ballet, conducted in full evening-dress and preceded by a solitary supper of two boiled eggs, became the highlight of his London summer and his only brush with the revelries of the Season. Back drinking tea in the solitude of Raymond Buildings, Theobalds Road, he reflected on these few glittering evenings where everyone seemed to know each other as if at some 'enormous but exclusive party'. Plaintively he wondered if he too might have been invited had he been 'a real rich Sassoon'. He felt strongly the desire 'to be youthful with the young . . . light-hearted before it was too late'.

One day when Sassoon was at a particularly low ebb, following an unpleasant interview with his family solicitor (during which he had failed to wheedle out an extra advance from his trust), he became aware, as he returned downcast to Raymond Buildings, 'of a fair-haired, hatless young man who had passed me . . . swinging along. Something unusual about him drew my attention. He looked so self-contained and carefree.' When the young man turned into Eddie Marsh's entrance, Sassoon knew who it was. 'So I've really seen the wonderful Rupert at last I thought, climbing rather wearily to my rooms. Somehow or other, he had made me feel a failure.'

The next morning Sassoon breakfasted with Rupert Brooke in Marsh's flat. He emerged chastened by the comparison feeling self-consciously a 'hard-boiled sportsman' and very amateur poet. Clad in open sandals, old flannel trousers and an open-necked shirt, the tousle-haired Brooke gazed serenely out of the window while, with an air of languid tolerance, he answered Sassoon's questions on his travels. Self-conscious of his own appearance as a philistine hunting-man, Sassoon's apologetic conclusion was that he was one of 'the procession of people who were more interested in [Brooke] than he was in them . . . There he was, aloof in his unforeseeingness of what was to come after, just a little weary of me, but all beautifully polite while he waited for me to go away.'

Yet Sassoon's mood of restlessness that summer had much in common with Brooke's. 'All that summer,' Sassoon recalled later in *The Weald of Youth*, 'I was accompanied by a feeling – not unconnected with the physical richness of youth – that I was on the verge of some experience which might liberate me from my blind alley of excessive sport and self-imposed artistic solitude.' Rupert Brooke was similarly dissatisfied with his life. His return in June 1914 from America caused him to yearn periodically for the New World. 'I am leading a fragmentary life,' he wrote to the wife of a Berkeley professor. 'As soon as I get to London, I want to be out in the country . . . and when I'm there, I'm looking up the next train to London to lunch with some friend I haven't seen for eighteen months.' 'One's too bally restless to work,' he confided elsewhere. 'All very dull. Wish to God I was married.'

On July 1 the annual river regatta at Henley had started – 'one fourth racing,' said an observer, 'and three fourths a brilliant *al fresco* picnic.' Along the banks punts and small boats were jammed together, bobbing up and down in the shadow of large and gaily decorated houseboats. Girls strolled in flower-trimmed hats, escorted by youths sportsmanlike in boaters, blazers and white trousers. 'One lounges and laughs,' wrote one participant appreciatively, 'from one dish of strawberries and cream to another through days of sheer content, when an exciting finish serves to justify – as though it needed any justification – one's absolute idleness.' For the first time Americans dominated the finals, when Harvard beat Boston on what was described as a 'lukewarm' Thames. 'Henley by motor,' an observer noted in the *Spectator*. 'Lunch at Leander Club. In punt, very hot. Feel very seedy.' After dinner, fireworks lit up the river scene while the crowds watched from a tow-path lit by Chinese lanterns.

Nearby, on a curve of the river above Windsor and Maidenhead, Nancy Astor held her annual Henley house-party at Cliveden. Surrounded by a broad terrace, the house sat imposingly on its hill overlooking the Thames, a Victorian palace built in 1850 for the Duke of Sutherland by the eminent architect Charles Barry; now a fitting home for one of the world's richest families. The beautiful, light-hearted Virginian, Nancy Astor, had become its châtelaine on her marriage to Waldorf in 1906, when her father-in-law William Waldorf Astor presented it to the newly-weds as a wedding gift. He included all his beloved furniture, such as the table, chairs and sideboard made for Madame de Pompadour's hunting-lodge at Asnières. Nancy immediately (if we are to believe her niece Nancy Lancaster's description of her) swept through this funereal Victorian grandeur like 'an electric light switched on suddenly in a room lit by candles'. Wholesale, she removed mosaic floors and ceiling frescoes, Roman busts, classical statues and sarcophagi. 'The keynote of the place when I took over,' she wrote in 1951, 'was splendid gloom. Tapestries and ancient leather furniture filled most of the rooms. The place looked better when I had put in books and chintz curtains and covers, and flowers.'

[92]

In the summer of 1914 Nancy was recovering her health and spirits after two operations. She was playing golf and tennis and enjoying the grounds of Cliveden, well maintained by a staff of over forty gardeners. Her footman of the time, Edwin Lee, later described the sumptuous scale of life at the Astor's country home, where they spent most of the early and mid-summer weekends. August and September 1914 they planned to spend as usual at their Scottish estate in Glen Coe. 'A fairly large staff was kept in both London and Cliveden,' wrote Lee, recalling balls, two or three each Season, for six hundred guests, and one reception to which a thousand people were invited. 'But most of us used to travel between London and Cliveden . . . At that time we had a very fine French chef . . . who was considered one of the best in the country . . . He had five girls working with him. We also had a stillroom where all the bread and cakes were made. Baking was done at Cliveden twice a week. There [were] . . . about ten or twelve stablemen. All the lawns on the pleasure grounds were mowed by horses with leather boots strapped over their iron shoes. In the house at Cliveden there was a housekeeper, six housemaids, six laundry maids and always one or two left in the kitchen apart from the travelling staff, also an Odd Man who used to look after the boilers, carry coal, answer the telephone – a most useful man in every way.'

Walter Elliot wrote a memoir which recalled Cliveden gatherings in 1920 immediately after the war. It can be read also for an idea of what the house must have been like in the pre-war days. 'Cliveden,' he wrote, 'was never more itself than in the dusk, on the high paved terrace outside its drawing-room windows . . . one always looked for the fireflies, and listened for the grasshoppers – and the mosquitos.'

Tea on summer weekends was 'laid out with infinite detail, under a pavilion roof at the end of the broad terrace. Tea, did I say? It was more like a Bedouin encampment. There was a table for tea, a table for cakes, a table for children, a table for grown-ups, a table for more grown-ups, and generally a nomadic group coming and going somewhere in the neighbourhood of Nancy herself. Cushions, papers, people, were mixed in a noble disarray . . .

'Somehow or other the party evolved, arranged itself, separated and came together again, re-arrayed for dinner . . . Nancy, teetotal to the core, never, for all that, attempted to impose her beliefs on her friends. The long table was laden with good food and drink. Twenty

[93]

people were a small gathering; forty was not unknown. Conversation was general – again, did I say conversation? – it was a debate, it was a riot, it was a tidal wave, in the midst of which small islets might be seen holding out determinedly in private talk till they too were borne away by the ever-rolling flood . . . After dinner . . . if Nancy were in one of her wilder moods, then . . . acting, games, impersonations of everything in or out of the world . . .'

On Saturdays Nancy would 'gird herself for exercise – tennis or golf – and sally forth, after some high-pitched objurgations against those who remained . . . in one of the rooms. "Why don't you all go out, what do you want to sit around here for? Go out! Go Out!! Look at the lovely day. Or at any rate go into some of my nice rooms, where I have the flowers . . ."

'Then she would go, hurrying like a deer . . . a figure of physical beauty to take the breath from your throat . . .'

The short Saturday-to-Monday country weekend was a new habit which the mobility bestowed by the motor car had encouraged. Lady Randolph Churchill also blamed American female influence: their restlessness encouraged 'what [I myself] was guilty of – motor from the country, dine at the Ritz, go to a play, and then to a Court Ball in the same gown!' An anonymous writer in *Country Life* bemoaned the loss of those 'peaceful summer weekends' in London, spent strolling in Hurlingham or Ranelagh Gardens; meeting one's friends by the Achilles statue or in the Ladies' Mile. Sunday church was invariably followed by a small lunch-party and a drive. 'Monday,' the writer concluded, 'always found me fresh and eager . . . Headaches and nerve storms were troubles of which my friends and I knew little . . .' But 'today all the machinery of social life has been "speeded up" . . . to the fatigue of the week, the labour of the weekend has now been added.'

The conscientious 1914 hostess, according to *Country Life*, left town on Friday well before her guests, 'very jaded and eager for a rest'. Instead, 'as soon as the country is reached and I have had some lunch, the cook and the housekeeper to say nothing of the telephone, demand a couple of hours.' On Saturdays while the men played golf, she had excursions planned for the female guests to organize. When it came to luncheon 'the telephone and the motor-car between them leave . . . constant doubt about the precise number of people who will be found at the table.' Similarly, Sunday breakfast was a 'perpetual feast' as the household came and went, some to early and some to late morning service. On Mondays the hostess bid her guests farewell and prepared for another house-party the following weekend.

As a result, the writer complained, at weekends, 'Clock golf, or a game of croquet or an hour or two on the tennis court are all I can manage. For the rest I am well satisfied if I can give an hour in each day to the garden, and even this is not always possible.' It was all right for the man 'who has no further duty than the signing of a monthly cheque . . . He gets his tennis or his golf, his billiards and bridge . . . and for him the change from town is a real rest . . .' Because, she added, 'I am a devoted wife I leave my little protest unsigned.' However, she warned her readers, 'Frankly, I think we women are trying to do too much nowadays. If we are to live the strenuous town life in May, June and July, we must in fairness to ourselves, use the country for relaxation.' As it was, after an 'attack of nerves' in 1912, she had had to spend a month's seclusion in an Austrian hideaway. Her next advice to *Country Life* readers would be on 'Modern women, the disease of restlessness and the art of "letting go".'

What of the guests who were causing their hostesses such nervous prostration? Pearl Barrington Crake went away 'almost every weekend if I was asked', motoring or taking long cross-country train journeys to each house-party. 'One usually travelled with a maid and there were no corridors on the train, so you had to be fearfully particular which carriage you got into.' She remembers helping her hostess arrange the drawing-room for a dance; huge jig-saw puzzles spread out on tables to amuse the guests; palatial stable-blocks with 'beaming grooms'.

'Coming down to breakfast one whole sideboard would groan with cold hams, cold tongue, cold pheasant if it was the season, cold chicken. That was by the way. The main sideboard held enormous silver chafing-dishes with the crest as a handle. Eggs and bacon were under one; kedgeree under another; kippers under another still. All the men who came in lifted them up. There was never a servant in at breakfast, never ever. And then the table was laid out with scones and rolls and marmalade. If the men were going out, they had a big breakfast and then they had a very big dinner. When they came in, they nearly always had poached eggs for their tea. My uncle ate a very large breakfast at, say, half past eight. My sister and I came down early with him and saw it in all its glory before it had been broken into. After breakfast the footman came in with a little square packet of greaseproof paper with a little piece of red tape and one sandwich and one ginger biscuit placed there. And a minute silver flask which had whisky or cherry brandy or whatever in it – that was all he was going to have till he got in about five.

'At dinner you were brought up by your mother to be very careful how much you drank. You had to be especially careful of the butler who, wanting to have lots of half-empty glasses, would go round the table and keep on filling them up. Another girl said to me, "Every time I look down, my glass seems to be full." She taught me to put my hand across. My uncle always used to have champagne on Saturday nights and he always said he drank to wives and sweethearts, looking at me across the table. I, aged seventeen, would blush to the roots of my hair.'

Cynthia Asquith, a Coterie acquaintance who was married to the Prime Minister's younger son, has conjured up for us a vivid picture of summer 'Saturday-to-Monday parties' before the war. In London her clothes were carefully selected and organised: three evening dresses, tea-gowns, a best dress and hat for church, '. . . a variety of country hats and caps . . . rows of indoor and outdoor shoes . . . numberless accessories in the way of petticoats, shawls, scarves, ornamental combs and wreaths, and a large bag in which to carry your embroidery about the house . . .' All this, she points out, 'necessitated at least one huge domed trunk called a Noah's Ark, an immense hat-box and a heavy dressing-case'. They had to be 'got in' to the motor-car by youths outside in the street, who then lived up to their nickname of 'street-runners' by pursuing the car to the station to unload it. The train itself might be a special one for the house-party. On board, certain fashionable guests would be recognisable by their green lockable travelling-cases from Vickerys of Bond Street. Maids generally carried the leather jewel-cases to match. At the other end, a waiting car collected guests from the country station. It might mean, Cynthia Asquith recalled, 'being crammed in with total strangers'.

Before her marriage, these house-parties were obviously an ordeal for her, dogged as she was by fear of 'being late for dinner . . . running short of conversation', even 'serving double faults at tennis'. On arrival, a long walk across the green lawns would find tea and the assembled house-party waiting for her, seated on wicker chairs, the men in flannels and straw boaters, the girls in muslin or linen frocks.

Wimbledon Ladies Final. Mrs Lambert Chambers.

Ulric Nisbet with his parents and sister (foreground), Prize-day,
Marlborough College, 1914.

Henley Regatta, July 1st 1914.

Hop-pickers in Kent.

After tea came the relaxing 'children's hour' when the denizens of nursery and schoolroom appeared to reap their small share of parental attention. As the guests joined in games of Hunt the Thimble and Here We Go Round the Mulberry Bush, the formality of the tea table dissolved inevitably into an informal mêlée of children and dogs.

Inside the house 'jugs of iced lemonade' set by 'great bowls of crimson roses' revived those who had come in from croquet or tennis. When the latecomers wandered upstairs, they would find their evening clothes laid out for them; their baths run; even the bath salts ready. Dinner of at least seven courses presented more conversational hurdles. In her desperate attempts to ward off silence, Cynthia Asquith recalls firing questions at her neighbours round the dinner table: 'Which do you like best, red or blue? Schiller or Goethe? Croquet or tennis?'

For Cynthia Asquith breakfast – still in 1914 the lavish Edwardian feast of yesteryear – remained a potent reminder of the pre-war country-house way of life. Her memories of the food served are tender, almost lyrical: '. . . an array of lidded silver dishes whereunder little blue flames kept piping hot curly rashers of bacon; eggs – poached, fried and scrambled – mounds of moist kedgeree, haddocks afloat in melted butter, sizzling, bursting sausages, ruddily-exuding kidneys . . . The finest trenchermen first lined themselves with porridge immersed in thick yellow cream and then piled on to their plate something out of practically every dish. After this they rammed down scones buttered two inches thick, and lavishly topped with marmalade, honey or home-made jam. This . . . was followed by fruit.'

Having painted this Lucullan scene for them, she then scoffs at the 1950's women reading her newly-published book. Unlike this modern generation, *her* contemporaries did not 'sustain themselves for the wear and tear of a whole morning's idleness on only a glass of orange-juice and a triangle of toast. Far from it . . . yet practically every girl's waist measured less than twenty inches.'

Cynthia Charteris as she was before she married Herbert Asquith, was the daughter of Lord and Lady Elcho, whose own rambling, hospitable country home was at Stanway in Gloucestershire. Guests were plentiful – 'Mama never seemed to have her own house to herself' – and return invitations were pressing. Cynthia and her brother Hugo (Ego), recently married to Diana Manners' sister

Violet, stayed at Avon Tyrell, the Lutyens house built for John Manners' family. They were frequently at Taplow with the Desboroughs and with the Horners at Mells. All these houses, according to Cynthia Asquith, provided a strikingly different atmosphere. The Manners were physical, 'Amazonian', eager horsemen, who expected their guests to play hockey and round up New Forest ponies. Through Lady Desborough, Taplow had become a showcase for poets, diplomats, statesmen, 'all the spirited youth'. Conversation and games, both athletic and intellectual, keyed the competition 'up to concert pitch'. Etty Desborough herself played games till midnight, then retired to talk the small hours away with her female guests. By contrast Cynthia Asquith was one of many who relished the walled garden, delicious food and peace of Mells, where Frances Horner, surrounded by bulb catalogues and stitching at her embroidery-frame, was a reassuring and restful presence.

Cynthia Asquith would not, one imagines, have had the same sentiments towards the indiscreet, immature and childishly impetuous woman who was her mother-in-law. 'Poor Margot,' she wrote of her. 'Her indiscretions are so naive, so childlike [that] I always resent her ... more in theory than in practice.' In 1914 Margot was fifty years old and had been the Prime Minister's wife since 1908. In 1912, impelled by dislike of Number 10 which she found 'liver-coloured . . . squalid' and impossible to entertain in, she persuaded Henry Asquith to buy a country home of his own. The Wharf at Sutton Courtenay near Oxford was a cramped, unpretentious house that had once been an inn. Its drawbacks were many but to Asquith it became and remained a great boon for the rest of his parliamentary life.

The Prime Minister's weekend routine was to leave London on Saturday, lunch at Skindles Hotel, Maidenhead, then play golf at Huntercombe. In the early evening he reached the Wharf, to be greeted by Margot's 'menagerie' of society guests.

The dining-room at the Wharf was nearly always crowded to capacity and filled with noise and smoke which rose to the rafters. Margot, whose own harsh, low-pitched voice generally dominated, once even called in a builder to try to deaden the din. Asquith, who preferred erudition to Margot's brand of 'clever' conversation, despised what he called society women with 'lending-library minds ... There is a sort of non-stop stupidity,' he wrote in his diary, 'among the upper classes, which I find exceedingly exhausting.' As a result, he singled out with delight the rare occasions when 'there was a nice old Papist don from Oxford staying in the house.' But he did admit to deriving amusement from the incongruity of Margot's 'rarely mixed' assortments of guests. 'We had the usual menagerie to lunch,' he commented on one occasion. 'A curious lunch party even for us.' Or once again: 'As incongruous a lot as even we have got together since Pierpont Morgan sat between Frau [the German governess] and Elizabeth.'

At these 'scratch dinner parties', Churchill, Edwin Montagu and the younger members of the government were frequent guests, mingling with the Listers, Parsons, and Manners, who were the friends (staying in the pretty Mill House across the village street) of the Asquith children. Asquith, in need of constant entertainment, was apt to sulk if he could not get a game of bridge. Rain was equally unwelcome. 'The weather was vile,' he wrote of one weekend when the Churchills were present. 'We could not golf – only trundle about at a snail's pace (in deference to Clemmie's fears) in a shut-up motor.' The last July weekend at the Wharf before the war was typical in its casual informality. Asquith, having soothed himself with Skindles and a round of golf, arrived at Sutton Courtenay to find 'no guest here so far except Montagu and Bongie [Bonham Carter] who arrived just in time for dinner ... The Somersets and Ottoline [Morrell] arrive some time today – just for the night ... Between now and Tuesday I have to think out something to say about the Amending Bill.' 'Most of the talk,' Ottoline Morrell's diary entry read, 'was about the assassination of the Crown Prince. Of all those present, only Edwin Montagu paced up and down and seemed disturbed. He said, "I suppose we shall have to go to war sooner or later with Germay about the Navy, and this may be as good a time as any other ..."'

In London the Season was drawing to a close. It had been, Ottoline Morrell recalled of 1914 in her memoirs, 'a very delightful summer ... Everything seemed to move with an odd ease and brilliance. London seemed indeed to be having a season such as it had not known for many years. Distinguished foreigners flocked here ... Our little *salon* in Bedford Square shared in the gaiety and glory, for it was beginning to be known as a centre for artists and some of the foreign visitors found their way to us.'

By birth Lady Ottoline Cavendish-Bentinck and by marriage the wife of Philip Morrell, a well-known Liberal M.P., Ottoline Morrell had an automatic entrée into most of London society. But she preferred her own Bloomsbury soirées where on Thursday evenings she gathered 'people together who have something "real" in them . . . free from foolish gossip and spite, that seems to be the chief topic of most London drawing-rooms'. To her grey-walled Bloomsbury drawing-room with its yellow taffeta curtains, she invited old friends like the Asquiths and the German art-lover Count Harry Kessler, and newer ones – Desmond MacCarthy and Lytton Strachey, at this stage in his career an unpopular and even derided figure. Fashionable society did not come. They considered the Morrells 'an odd couple' and anyway, they would upset the harmony and unselfconscious gaiety, said Ottoline Morrell. But artists did, and writers, and the group of intellectuals who in months to come would form a nucleus of pacifists around Ottoline's strongly pacifist husband. (Later, the Morrells' country home at Garsington in Oxfordshire became a famous haven for Conscientious Objectors to the war.) But as yet the Morrells' gatherings were light-hearted and carefree affairs. Ottoline's 'instinctive passion' was for people to meet and be friends, to discuss politics, art and poetry. 'I should like this house to become a centre,' was her plea in her diary on June 1 1914. 'I so much desire to give real friendship' – whereupon she threw open her two large reception rooms ('the gay in one room and the sedate talkers . . . in the other').

Ottoline went in search of rewarding friendships too. She took under her wing artists like Stanley Spencer, then living in a semi-detached house in Cookham. In a borrowed evening suit, long sleeved, his coat-tails drooping, Spencer was launched upon the artistic world. Beside him Ottoline in her capacious black silk cloak, hovered protectively 'like a great hen'. To soothe his shyness, she often took his parents and brother out with him, disregarding (with a lack of snobbishness rare at the time) their 'ruddy' faces and 'unkempt hair'. Alone, she ventured to Spitalfields to see Mark Gertler, a young Jewish painter still living with his family of fur-sewers in Whitechapel. Later she took Sickert and Jasper Ridley to see his work. Finally, Ottoline was a frequent visitor to the building at Number 8, Fitzroy Street which housed both Augustus John's and Whistler's studios. 'How ramshackle and dark and dirty [was] the hall of this house of studios,' was her comment. 'An elegant gold console table in the hall, letters scattered about on it. Up and up and along rickety passages, down steps and up others – at last, after groping and peering, we find a piece of paper pinned to a door, "Augustus John".

'What fun it all was,' she concluded, 'that summer. Everything seemed easy and light, as if the atmosphere had something electric and gay in it.'

The fashionable world that Ottoline Morrell professed to dislike was meantime making the most of the dying Season. The Eton against Harrow match took place on July 10 in sunshine hot enough to raise the parasols of the watching mamas lined up along the boundary lines in landaus and motors. The parasols were fringed with light or dark blue tassels; cornflowers sprouted in button-holes; blue flags and handkerchiefs waved. The Archbishop of Canterbury was among almost twenty thousand spectators who saw Eton triumph as the Duke of Devonshire's crowded box went wild with delight. Outside the pavilion groups of boys, light or dark blue scarves wound round their silk top-hats, shouted the name of their school and 'hat-bagged' or 'tile-tapped' their rivals. The 'rag' continued in the grounds of the Exhibition at Earl's Court where the families gathered to celebrate that evening, trying out the sideshows or dancing with each other's sisters to a Guards band. Fathers and uncles joined in. There was friendly tussling round the Helter-Skelter and the Water Chute. At the Joy Wheel a tug-of-war between the schools took place. It was late at night before the crowds of young people, including now the Prince of Wales who had arrived halfway through the evening, finally and happily dispersed.

On July 16th the last pre-war Court Ball was held at Buckingham Palace. Two thousand guests waltzed to Strauss under the magnificent chandeliers. The previous evening many of the same people had danced at the home of the Speaker of the House of Commons, among them several young officers who would soon be fighting in France. On the 18th the Marchioness of Salisbury opened up her mansion in Arlington Street. At her ball the great rooms were filled with the scent of flowers sent up from the greenhouses of Hatfield.

Towards the end of July the thought of holidays and countryside beckoned. Mrs Asquith gave a garden party at Downing Street. Mr Balfour light-heartedly took it upon himself to lecture on tennis at the Unionist garden party held at Panshanger. In the wake of this celebration hosted by the Desboroughs, a flood of similar political garden parties followed. The guests who travelled to them by train could count on silken cords to separate them from the riff-raff at the station. In magazines and in newspapers the rural theme was everywhere in evidence. 'Tired to death', proclaimed one disgruntled party-goer in *Vanity Fair*, while another sighed over *How the Country Changes one's Personality*, and *Country Life* discussed *The Reversion to Simplicity*. Alongside, advertisements tempted the reader with thoughts of 'Summer in Normandy' or Scotland or Bavaria or with 'Holiday Books for the Holiday Mood'. 'Poppyland' was the name given in one advertisement to England's 'glorious' East coast. The flower was innocent still of the sinister associations it would inspire a few years after the end of the war.

For Diana Manners and her circle July 1914 was marred by a tragedy which seemed to them afterwards to pull down the curtain on their joyous pre-war world and usher in a life of sorrow and apprehension which was to be theirs to endure for the next four years. They had been one rainy July evening to a party at the Russian Embassy – Edward Horner, Raymond and Katharine Asquith, Duff Cooper and Diana Manners, Denis Anson, Sybil Hart-Davis and Iris Tree. Afterwards with Constantine Benckendorf, son of the Russian Ambassador, and some others, they hired a launch for a night cruise along the Thames. There was supper and dancing to a quartet from Thomas Beecham's orchestra. 'Who suggested bathing?' wrote Diana Manners later in her autobiography. 'I cannot tell. It may, it *may* have been me – I have so prayed that it was not and now I do not know. Anyway, no-one was keener or more pleased at the project than I was.' Whatever the truth of this, the fact was that Denis Anson (who had been 'swinging in the rigging' before the launch started) jumped in the water immediately. To Diana Manners' screams of horror he was seen almost at once to be in difficulties. Constantine Benckendorf and a bandsman both leapt to his aid. Though the launch had stopped, only the Ambassador's son was eventually rescued, worn out, though he was a strong swimmer, by the much stronger tide. It seemed to Diana Manners unbelievable. 'Dripping and haggard', she went with the rest in the hope of finding Denis Anson at his flat.

In the public inquest which followed Diana Manners received from the press a great deal of acrimony and from the Anson family much of the blame. F. E. Smith appeared for her party, called to their aid by Edward Horner who was in his chambers. 'I was held guiltiest,' she wrote, 'as being the most conspicuous. The travesties of truth told against me stimulated me to ideas of retaliation, but it was now July, and August 1914 was very near.

'The young musician was consumptive and was due to die,' she could reassure herself. 'The Great War was upon us and Denis would surely have been the first to be killed.' Nevertheless, 'this was a gruesome, soul-shattering end to the carefree life I knew.' To Duff Cooper, very close to Denis Anson, this was at twenty-four, 'the first great sorrow of my life. I had hardly emerged from it,' he recollected, 'when the war broke out.'

In the latter half of July, Siegfried Sassoon returned to the country from London. Yet another empty, inactive summer day in the capital had found him taking a walk in Regent's Park. The listless animals – penguins 'wilting in the heat'; lions and tigers 'prowling restlessly about'; a monkey who gazed and 'sighed and looked away [as if] wondering why either of us was there' – added to Sassoon's sense of lonely futility. Shortly afterwards a friend whom he had tried to impress with his hectic social life guessed the truth when he arrived back at his solitary lodgings for tea. Sassoon packed and left for Weirleigh, clutching the scores of *Boris Godunov* and *Prince Igor* among his belongings. He had expected the flat in Raymond Buildings to be his home for at least three years. As it happened, twenty-seven years were to pass before he returned in 1941.

Once again Sassoon was installed in his lofty studio overlooking a Kentish garden, writing by day, and playing *Boris Godunov* by candlelight in the drawing-room in the evening, with the windows open to catch the night scent of flowers. He drove to Tunbridge Wells in a dog-cart past apple orchards where small boys hired to protect the fruit shouted and chattered. He played golf at Lamberhurst to the sound of sheep-bells and a river meandering through the greens. Each morning his 'old friend, the milk train' woke him, 'puffing away from Paddock Wood station'. Then, happy to be home, he would 'slip on some clothes and creep downstairs, while the grandfather clock in the hall ticked indulgently . . . and the high window by the carved oak linen cupboard showed a brightening east through leaded panes . . .' Standing on the doorstep outside the drawing-room with 'some ordinary day of youth' ahead of him, Sassoon would feel that summer, 'all the goodness of being alive'.

While Sassoon played tennis on summer afternoons at Weirleigh, or bicycled to Rye for golf and a tea of eggs and jam sandwiches, Bessie Ellis sweltered in the hot vicarage with its glowing coal-fire range. 'We wore so many clothes – vests, boned corsets, liberty bodice, cambric knickers, a white petticoat and stockings we knitted ourselves. Once or twice we did go bathing, but that was almost as bad. You wore a bathing-dress down to your ankles with trousers underneath, a high neck and long sleeves. Only the gentry got the sun on their skins. We never saw it.'

The fruit-pickers down from London gave the staff a taste of the world outside the confines of church and vicarage. 'They were foreign, the pickers, from the East End mostly. They came for two or three weeks in July. It was their yearly holiday. They had bonfires in the open fields and cooked on a big fire. They ran a shop for them on the farm and they slept in barns or huts. They went to the pub drinking and had enormous sing-songs in the evening. Some of them were gypsies, looked down on by the East Enders. They poached but were very quick. They used to chase us and we got frightened. There was never a swede or a cabbage left when they were around let alone a damson or a plum.'

So the days of July drew on, and within a few miles of each other young Mr Sassoon from Weirleigh, and the vicar's youngest, rawest servant Ellis, breathed the same Kentish air, but knew nothing of each other or of their totally different lives. Yet they were content enough in their separate worlds, making the best of their certainty that nothing could or would ever change. Already Bessie had set her quick Irish wits to learning the duties of a housemaid. With marriage to her 'young man' from Pembury and perhaps a cottage with a lean-to washhouse, she would have 'bettered' herself, she told herself during the summer months of 1914, 'as much as I knew how'.

For Sassoon life that summer could have been expected to progress in years to come in much the same leisurely, gentlemanly, comfortable manner, once he had obtained the £500 he needed urgently to pay his debts and set him 'straight'. Neither he nor Bessie could have foretold the way in which two years hence their fortunes would change and their lives touch each other, when Sassoon – 'a poor wreck with nerves and almost ate up with lice' – returned from the Front and Bessie, promoted to the Weirleigh staff, was one of those who nursed him.

If Sassoon's experience of London life had been a bitter one, Rupert Brooke had had a brilliant season. Under Edward Marsh's auspices he went everywhere and met everyone of interest to him. He breakfasted with Stanley Spencer; lunched with Henry James;

supped with J. M. Barrie at the Savoy; accompanied Gaudier-Brzeska to the ballet at Drury Lane. Lady Ottoline Morrell asked Brooke to her receptions; he was invited to dine and to recitations at Number 10. On July 25, the day after Austria's declaration of war on Serbia, Brooke lunched with D. H. Lawrence and his wife Frieda at The Ship. Their host, Edward Marsh, arrived breathless and excited. 'I believe Sir Edward Grey has just prevented war with Germany!' he proclaimed. But that evening Brooke dined at Number 10, Downing Street. The Prime Minister, seated next to him, was present while Winston Churchill offered from across the table to help Brooke find a commission. The next morning Brooke left to spend his twenty-seventh birthday with his mother at Rugby. One day later, a letter arrived from there for Edward Marsh. It ended with a question. 'Do you have a Brussels-before-Waterloo feeling that we'll all – or some – meet with other eyes in 1915?'

It was not until the last week of July that the European crisis worsened to the extent that politicians and press were forced at last to drag their attention away from the Irish crisis. On July 24 the British Cabinet were preoccupied once again with Ireland, where civil war loomed and private armies from north and south were openly drilling. The Cabinet were interrupted in their inconclusive debate by, as Winston Churchill has recalled, 'the quiet grave tones of Sir Edward Grey's voice . . . reading a document which had just been brought to him from the Foreign Office. It was the Austrian note to Serbia. He had been reading or speaking for several minutes before I could disengage my mind from the tensions and bewildering debate which had just closed. We were all very tired, but gradually as the phrases and sentences followed one another, impressions of a wholly different character began to form in my mind. This note was clearly an ultimatum; but it was an ultimatum such as had never been penned in modern times. As the reading proceeded it seemed absolutely impossible that any state in the world could accept it, or that any acceptance, however abject, would satisfy the aggressor. The parishes of Fermanagh and Tyrone faded back into the mists and squalls of Ireland, and a strange light began immediately but by perceptible gradations to fall and grow upon the map of Europe.'

The Austrian ultimatum to Serbia, despite the virtual acceptance of its humiliating terms by the Serbian government, had brought about, noted Asquith in his diary on July 26, 'the most dangerous situation for the last forty years'. Should Russian troops go to the support of their fellow-Slavs in Serbia, the Germans would join against Russia with their Austrian ally. If Russia was attacked, France was bound by treaty to go to her aid. Such a chain of deadly circumstances could not but fail to involve Britain, if only to make her decide (she had no alliance with any of these Powers obliging her go to to war, the Prime Minister had declared in 1913) to remain non-aligned.

Such a course of deliberate non-involvement was the one still advocated by three quarters at least of the Members of the House of Commons who, pointing out the brutality and savagery of Russia and the instability of France, questioned the wisdom of putting at risk on their behalf the peace and prosperity of by far the richest country in Europe. On the other hand, there were others firm in their belief in both the Liberal and Conservative parties that even *without* a treaty Britain must support the French, 'as an honourable expectation had been raised'. 'I hate it, I hate it!' said Sir Edward Grey as he saw his Prime Minister's worst fears being realised. 'It is the greatest step towards Socialism that could have been made. We shall have Labour Governments in every country after this.' Nevertheless, each day at the Foreign Office, he was confronted with the distressing spectacle of the distracted French Ambassador, Monsieur Cambon, pleading for British help for his country's cause. Despite the non-interventionists many agreed with the Prime Minister's wife, Margot Asquith, who seeing the German and Russian Ambassadors at a reception together, is reputed to have remarked at this time: 'Only those two old fools between us and European war.'

At schools throughout Britain the end of July brought the end of the summer term with its farewells and speeches. Violet Graham attended Wellington Speech Day where her brother was a pupil, and the next evening, Sandhurst Ball.

'I remember a big marquee. We all wore white frocks, rather high-waisted. The Sandhurst boys filled up your programme before you got there. They had a swop system – "I'll dance with your sister if you dance with my cousin twice." We did the Lancers and the one-step and waltzes and polkas. We finished up with a gallop to John Peel. It was a jolly good dance. At the time I thoroughly enjoyed it. Later on, of course, it was terrible, looking back and thinking of all those bright, eager boys who had been killed.

'We took the train back to Wales and the newspapers were full of the crisis. My brother was very excited. We talked about it with my mother, wondering what an earth would happen.'

At another public school, Marlborough, Ulric Nisbet was one of those who 'said goodbye to Marlborough at the end of July 1914, fully expecting to be back again in September'. He remains convinced that none of his schoolboy contemporaries 'knew anything about the extreme gravity of the international situation. There was no radio or TV, of course, and at school we seldom saw, let alone read, a newspaper. We had grown up in a settled world. True, there was some sabre-rattling on the part of Germany and Lord Roberts' warnings of the German menace, presented theatrically in a play that I had greatly enjoyed, *An Englishman's Home*. But War with a capital W, in that age . . . of German bands . . . was inconceivable.'

Because he expected to be back, Ulric Nisbet was spared the 'emotional wrench' of the last chapel service 'when, in a curiously quiet way, voices united in the singing of "Lord, dismiss us with thy blessing"'. His thoughts at the time were of 'departing friends', whom he seemed to regard for the first time 'with the feelings of maturity instead of with the casual good-fellowship of youth'. The next day he was at Lords, playing against Rugby in a two-day cricket match. 'The air was full of people shouting, "Better luck next year", or "See you soon" to those we thought we'd see at Marlborough next term.' Then, 'I went home to my people, who had been in the East and were just retiring. I saw a headline on the way – "Twenty thousand Austrians have their retreat cut off." It seemed extraordinary. It was the end of July, and I did not know even then that there was going to be a world war.'

Anthony Eden, seventeen like Ulric and an Eton schoolboy, also went to his school's cricket match at Lords. Next day his brother Jack Eden introduced him to an heroic figure who had scored centuries for both Harrow and Cambridge there. Eden, Eton and Oxford, was 'as much impressed by this heroic feat as shocked by this double achievement for the wrong cause'. But the meeting was especially memorable in retrospect, when he knew that neither young man had more than six months to live.

Jack Eden, a twenty-six year-old moustached and monocled cavalry officer, was a dashing figure to his admiring younger brother. They were not close, having had little opportunity to be so, but in their brief meetings during July 1914, Jack proved friendly and kind. On the first day of Eton's Long Leave he drove Anthony by Daimler to the Cavalry Club, and introduced him to the officers who had served with him abroad. His friends clustered round discussing polo matches between regiments, leaving the nervous schoolboy speechless with shyness. The next day at Hurlingham Anthony and his mother watched Jack play for the 12th Lancers in the Subalterns' Cup. It was a beautiful day, Eden remembers, like a scene from Renoir with the 'hats like laden trays of the gaily dressed women'. When it was finished, Jack came to take his leave of them. He was killed during a cavalry patrol near Ypres in October and his brother never saw him again.

On July 28 as the crowds chanting patriotic songs gathered in Vienna, the Austro-Hungarian government put out its declaration of war on Serbia. Shortly afterwards began the bombardment of Belgrade. 'Of course Russia will rush to our aid!' was the reaction of the Serbian Legation in London. 'Russia is our dear brother, and we are bent upon fulfilling the dream of Napoleon and working towards a Slav Empire.' And indeed, a partial mobilization of the Russian forces was almost immediately under way.

On Tuesday July 28, as Europe reeled in turmoil, London Society was due to attend Goodwood, traditionally the last function of the Season. This year Goodwood Week proved a failure. There was reported the press, 'a general feeling of anxiety', heightened by the noticeable absence among the race-goers of the King. His horse won the opening race but he was not in the white Royal Pavilion inside the Grandstand Enclosure to watch it, nor did the Royal Standard float, as in previous years, over Goodwood House. His absence at the races was given out as being due to 'the serious European situation'.

Enough cars and omnibuses did cram the road to Goodwood race-course to stir up a cloud of white dust from the chalky downland soil. By the end of the week the numbers attending had dropped precipitously as the crisis deepened and worried house-party guests returned to their own homes.

Friday July 31 was the last day of the meeting. All over the course small groups huddled anxiously discussing the state of Europe and the probability of war. There were rumours of officers being recalled to their depots. The alarming news spread of the closure of the Stock Exchange for the first time in its history. The bank rate doubled from four to eight per cent. 'The City,' wrote Asquith, 'is in a terrible state of depression and paralysis ... The prospect is very bleak.' The ordinary citizen shared his mood of pessimism. All that day the banks were beseiged by queues of frightened depositors demanding to withdraw large sums in gold.

Anthony Eden was at a Public School Camp deep in the English countryside, having journeyed there from London in the light grey uniform with its pale blue facings of Eton OTC. The talk in the camp was all of war: would there be one? Would they fight? For how long? Perhaps in the light of the circumstances the training seemed more arduous than the previous year's, with two all-day exercises and even one at night. Such was the hunger for news that the boys walked outside the camp gates each evening to where the late newspaper editions were on sale. One of the masters, a platoon commander, tried to laugh their apprehension away. 'There won't be any war,' he told them. 'The City would never allow it. Even if fighting did break out, it couldn't be more than a few days, the money would run out.' But as July ended, the boys woke one morning to find that he, along with the instructors, the Adjutant, even the army cooks had gone. The boys themselves were swiftly marched to the station to the tune of *Tipperary*. They were eager, Anthony Eden recalls, but not excited, having no comprehension of what war actually meant. In any case, it seemed certain from what had been told them, to be over in six months, and during that time Anthony Eden, at any rate, knew where his destiny lay. In the autumn he would go back to Eton. For the summer, he would return to the quiet – 'hushed and sombre as though someone were dead in the house already' – of his home at Windlestone in County Durham.

'Only during this last weekend in July,' says a contemporary, 'did the average family have any inkling of the danger. Suddenly as they opened their papers, they were confronted not with Ireland but with European war.' 'On the Brink of War!' 'Europe Drifting to Disaster' were the screaming headlines. In a matter of days at Madame Tussaud's Waxworks a new tableau had suddenly appeared on view: 'The Crisis of Europe, with Lifelike Portrait Models of King George, the Emperor of Austria, King Peter of Serbia, and Other Reigning Sovereigns.' At midnight on July 30, Russia had ordered full mobilization. In Britain the first military personnel on leave began to be recalled to their units. A cricket match at Lords broke up when all reservists were ordered to leave abruptly. At Tunbridge Wells the band of the Royal Irish Rifles, in the midst of playing at the Pantiles, received a telegram demanding their immediate recall. At

Lloyds all normal business had been suspended. Policies for war risks rocketed. Outside in the London streets large-scale maps of Europe sold to an anxious public. Fleet Street, according to Philip Gibbs, was humming with activity: 'Sub-editors emerging from little dark rooms with a new excitement in eyes that had grown tired with proof-correcting . . . It was a chance of seeing the greatest drama in life with real properties, real corpses, real blood, real horrors with a devilish thrill in them.' On the night of July 30 Gibbs himself, destined to be the war's foremost reporter, had caught a train to the Continent. The next day the French chefs at the House of Commons received call-up orders from Paris.

Margot Asquith, calling on the German Ambassador's wife, Princess Lichnowsky, found her 'lying on a green sofa with a dachshund by her side; her eyes were red and swollen from crying, and her husband was walking up and down wringing his hands. He caught me by the arm. "Oh, say it is not true, there's not going to be a war! Dear, dear Mrs Asquith, can nothing be done to prevent it?" The Princess got up and looked out of the window. "Look at this beautiful, wonderful England," she said, "and to think that we are going to fight against her."

'All that day,' Margot Asquith's recollection continued, 'my husband and Sir Edward Grey, the Foreign Secretary, were sending cables to Germany in the hope of finding a way out.' Their Cabinet colleague, Winston Churchill, was, reported Asquith, 'very bellicose, demanding instant mobilization'. He and his supporters pleaded the tragic cause of 'gallant little Belgium', whom both Britain and France had pledged to support in a treaty of 1839. In fact, moved by her desperate need to be seen to retain her strict neutrality, Belgium had already replied to an offer of help from France. 'We are sincerely grateful to the French government . . . In the actual circumstances, however, we do not propose to appeal to the guarantee of the Powers. The Belgian Government will decide later on the action they may think it necessary to take.'

It was not until August 3rd that the Belgian King telegraphed from Brussels to his fellow-monarch King George V, appealing to him in the name of friendship to intervene diplomatically to safeguard Belgium's neutrality. By then it was too late. Germany had declared war on Russia; the German army was poised to march on France. The long-prepared Schlieffen Plan had assured the German generals that their quickest route to victory lay through Belgium.

5

August

BRITAIN WENT TO WAR with Germany on the night of August 4, 1914, having received no reply to her ultimatum that German invasion troops be recalled from Belgium. As the deadline (11 p.m. in London; midnight in Berlin) approached, the excitement grew almost tangible in the crowds who had massed in the West End all day, filling Whitehall and Trafalgar Square, spilling into the Mall and Horseguards Parade, where the lights of the Foreign Office and Admiralty, still brilliantly lit at this late hour, shone down on them. In some places they turned ugly, a mob howling anti-German slogans and chanting 'We Want War!' But mostly, according to the diarist Harold Nicolson, the huge throng of straw-boatered men, and women in summer frocks and hats, was good-natured, 'throbbing . . . with excited optimism'. Cars passed decorated with French and British colours; in Bedford Square they were singing the Marseillaise; men queued up to shake the hands of those already in uniform; and everywhere Union Jacks waved. As the evening drew on and the numbers swelled, joined by the theatre and restaurant crowd in evening dress, the huge mass moved up the Mall to the gates of Buckingham Palace at the end. Here the King and Queen appeared to wave from the balcony, as their excited subjects war-whooped with delight. Duff Cooper later contrasted 'the hilarious crowd cheering the outbreak of war' on this day, with 'the silent and awe-stricken masses on the eve of the declaration of war in 1939'. Osbert Sitwell, from his vantage point in the Mall, as the hour struck, saw the crowd 'roar for its own death. It cheered and cried and howled . . .' In the Cabinet Room at Number 10 the Prime Minister Herbert Asquith could hear the commotion. 'War,' he observed bitterly, 'or anything that seems likely to lead to war is always popular with the London mob.'

Nevertheless, many in that London 'mob', swept up by the

powerful emotions of that extraordinary evening, must have woken next morning sober and subdued, to face the awesome reality of what had happened. Not everyone welcomed the war. Not only was there a deep suspicion of militarism in Nonconformist Liberal England – so that some Radicals even called for the Scouting Movement 'with its military overtones' to be abolished – but the Labour Movement too was strongly pacifist. In 1907 an International Socialist Conference agreed that, if war threatened, it was the binding duty of the working-class to prevent it, and failing that, to bring about a ceasefire as soon as possible. Class war was the only war conceivable here. In April 1914 at a conference of Britain's own Independent Labour Party, Keir Hardie turned to a group of Sunday schoolchildren seated behind his dais, and told them that two things in the world were unnecessary: poverty – and war.

Up till the last moment it looked as if socialist opposition to the war might hold. An emergency meeting of international socialist leaders was called during the last week in July. Keir Hardie attended for Britain and voiced his conviction that rather than mobilize, British transport workers would come out on strike. His confidence, bravely assumed in the face of the emergency, was utterly misplaced.

August 2 found Hardie addressing an anti-war rally during a downpour in Trafalgar Square. There was sympathetic support for him, and for Arthur Henderson, Secretary of the Labour Party, and only 'a small opposition of Jingoes'. On August 3 pleas for neutrality came from a group of Cambridge Fellows, backed up by a number of bishops. At the same time, a Neutrality Committee was being formed, which allied Ramsay MacDonald, Leader of the Labour Party, with such prominent intellectuals as the classicist Gilbert Murray, and the Oxford historian, Basil Williams. Too late, on August 5, the Neutrality League took out a full-page advertisement against the war in the *Daily News*. By now the tide amongst the socialists was turning.

Then, in the House of Commons, the Prime Minister made a powerful speech justifying the decision to lead the country into war. They went, he said, with a 'clear conscience' and a 'strong conviction that . . . [they were] fighting not for aggression, not for the maintenance of . . . selfish ends, but in defence of principles the maintenance of which [was] vital to the civilized world.

'We have a great duty to perform,' he continued. 'We have got a great truth to fulfil; and I am confident Parliament and the country will enable us to do it.' The Commons cheered, and unity among the socialists finally crumbled. Within days the *Daily News* dropped its anti-war stance to display first a grudging acceptance of the *status quo*, and then, like the rest of the country, a bellicose enthusiasm for it. As the Trade Unions and the Labour Party too swung wholeheartedly behind the war, Ramsay MacDonald, bitter but not convinced, resigned his leadership of the Labour Party. There were those in the Party who followed him, but to the vast majority of British workers, the call of nationalism was stronger than that of politics. Lining up beside their countrymen of every class, they turned their antagonism on to a common foe: the foreigners, the Germans.

There remained some Liberals against the war but Lloyd George, the former arch-pacifist, made one of the first stirring speeches calling his fellow-countrymen to arms. Reminding them of the 'forgotten peaks' of 'Honour, Duty and Patriotism', he singled out (prophetically, considering the war of attrition that would follow) 'the great pinnacle of Sacrifice ... clad in glittering white ... pointing like a rugged finger to Heaven'. Henceforth, as Minister of Munitions in 1915, and from 1916 Prime Minister, all the fires of his oratory would burn to one savage purpose.

There was another orator who might have been expected to speak out for peace, and whose voice would have been heeded, at least by his own kind. The Reverend John Clifford, a Nonconformist and former President of the National Free Church Council, had been a leader of the pacifists during the Boer War. He was, moreover, an imposing and well-respected figure (looking, according to Arthur Marwick, like 'a bearded Old Testament' prophet), and a familiar sight at Free Church conferences. He was at such a conference, on the Churches' Peace Alliance, very shortly before war broke out. When it did and he decided, on the grounds of German inhumanity and aggression, that it was his religious duty to support it, he must have swayed many church-goers on to his side.

One further protest meeting of note took place on the outbreak of war. On the evening of August 4, a Women's Meeting was held to show the women of the nation, at least, 'What War Would Mean'. Mrs Fawcett of the National Union of Women's Suffrage Societies addressed it. Days later, she offered the facilities of these societies to the embattled nation in its time of trial. The rebellious militants of the Women's Social and Political Union, veterans of violence and arson, weaned on prison and force-feeding, had been reborn overnight in the image of demure, patriotic womanhood. The 'defiant and insolent lawbreakers' who had outraged the press at the beginning of the year, became model daughters, sisters, wives, their one thought to support their men and the war effort. On 11 August it was announced that all their sentences would be remitted, His Majesty being confident that they would now avoid 'any further crime or disorder'. In return, suffragette leaders like Mrs Pankhurst and her daughter Christabel joined the recruiting drive. Platforms where they had once spat out threats against the establishment now rang to their exhortations to rise up and fight 'the German Peril'. Only Sylvia Pankhurst, Mrs Pankhurst's other daughter, refused to mend her ways in the Great Cause. Watching a shipload of reservists embark at Dublin, she found them 'incognisant as oxen; or wildly uproarious . . . glassy-eyed, purple of face, foul-mouthed . . . a writhing agglomeration of human folly . . . untouched by the cleansing fires of enthusiasm, going like cattle to be slaughtered'.

Had it been 1917 that Sylvia Pankhurst was writing about – a boatload of unseasoned, apprehensive conscripts going in to plug the huge gaps in the line caused by Passchaendale or the Somme – the dumb apathy and vituperative anger she perceived in these troops journeying to the Front, would seem altogether more likely. But this was 1914. The country, as Duff Cooper wrote later, was going to war 'in a mood of confidence and excitement . . . Men remembered the relief of Mafeking and of Ladysmith and the victory of Omdurman. It was generally felt that war was a glorious affair and the British always won.' Duff himself, prevented by his Foreign Office Superiors from joining up, was filled with envy and gloom at the sight of other 'civilian friends transformed overnight into officers with plenty of leisure and the prospect of exciting adventure' before them, while for him the war meant hours of extra work deciphering the mountains of telegrams in the Foreign Office cipher-room.

Meanwhile, outside in the streets amongst the crowds the mood of contagious excitement had not abated but had taken on the aspect of a patriotic crusade. Up and down the main thoroughfares of local towns, bands marched, rousing the citizens with martial music and beating the drum to increase the flow of new recruits. In the music-halls, stars like Phyllis Dare plucked the heart-strings of their audience and coaxed, or shamed, young men into joining up by singing sentimental patriotic songs. In her hometown, Buxton in

Derbyshire, Vera Brittain 'joined the excited little group round the Post Office' who watched 'a number of local worthies who had suddenly donned their Territorial uniforms and were driving importantly about in motor-cars with their wives or chauffeurs at the wheel'. It was all so exciting, Nancy Cunard was to recall later. 'I cannot think how we had such high spirits. Everything – war-work, weekends, parties seemed to go with such speed.' Their feelings would change when the convoys of real wounded started coming in, but for the moment it was fun for upper-class girls like Nancy Cunard and Diana Manners to dress up in VAD uniforms and go to bandaging classes. Pearl Barrington Crake remembers the first Red Cross classes as something of a social event. 'I went off to Red Cross Home Meeting Class,' she wrote in her diary for August, 'and found it so full we had to sit on the stairs. Mrs Vennings has lent her house in Cadogan Square for meetings.' 'Nobody knew what was happening,' she told the author later. 'We were all rushing around in circles. You see, it was the absolute peak of the Season.' Among the provincial society of Buxton, the excitement ran high also. 'For the next few weeks [after the outbreak of war],' recalled Vera Brittain scathingly, 'we all suffered from the epidemic of wandering about that had seized everyone in town . . . The polite female society of Buxton . . . rolled a few bandages and talked about the inspiration of helping one's country to win the War. One or two would-be leaders of fashion paraded continually through the town in new Red Cross uniforms. Dressed in their most elaborate lace underclothing, they offered themselves as patients to would-be bandagers and bed-makers . . .'

All over the country from cottage parlours to country-house drawing-rooms, there was a feverish epidemic of sock-knitting. So many pairs were sent in to the War Office, that the British Government tried to encourage a more useful channelling of energies to help the war effort. Female indignation was fierce. Faced with a public outcry the Government capitulated, announcing a plan to co-ordinate clothes production. Even Vera Brittain, contemputous as she was of the Buxton ladies' attempts to 'provincialise the War', tried her hand at knitting for the soldiers. But only 'for a very short time . . . I found the simplest bed-socks and sleeping-helmets altogether beyond me.'

However much she loathed 'this terrible War' – and she was perspicacious enough to fear its consequences most dreadfully – she could not help feeling left out of the excitement and exaltation which was obviously affecting her brother Edward and his friends. 'Women get all the dreariness of war and none of its exhilaration,' she observed to Roland gloomily, and was hurt when he brushed aside his earlier peacetime dreams of Oxford as irrelevant. 'I don't think in the circumstances I could easily bring myself to endure a secluded life of scholastic vegetation,' he confessed, trying to explain to her his urgent desire for a commission. Apart from it being 'a cowardly shirking of . . . duty' even to consider doing otherwise, he certainly 'did not want to miss this War. It is to me a very fascinating thing – something, if often horrible, yet very ennobling and very beautiful, something whose elemental reality raises it above the reach of all cold theorising. You will call me a militarist. You may be right.'

In those first heady days, joining up and appearing amongst the public in the King's uniform, brought immediate recognition, acclaim and satisfaction. On August 5, W. R. Colyer, an ex-public schoolboy recently out of Merchant Taylors', sat fuming with restlessness and impatience at his office desk. 'Would . . . [the Germans] invade us, I wondered. By George! If they should they'd find us a tougher nut to crack than they expected. My bosom swelled and I clenched my fist. I wished to goodness I were in the Army. I felt restless, excited, eager to do so something desperate for the cause of England.

'And then the impulse came, sending the blood tingling all over my body: why not join the Army now? A great and glorious suggestion . . .'

Later in the day, Colyer joined 'a roomful of fellows' at the Duke Street Headquarters of the Artists' Rifles. He signed on. 'I went home throbbing with a new vitality, as (I imagine) a man might who has just plighted his troth to the girl he had loved at first sight.' In the days that followed, stepping out, his rifle on his shoulder, to make his way home from training each evening, he reaped his reward. 'As I walked through the streets people looked admiringly at me, and I felt more than ever pleased with myself. Girls smiled at me, men looked at me with respect, the bus-drivers wished me luck and refused to take money for my fare, and everybody made way for me, as being on the King's business.'

Little wonder that other young men were desperate to join in. 'We thought it would be over by Christmas,' remembers Harold

Macmillan. 'Those of us who were not soldiers made frantic efforts to get in before the war ended.' In this climate of optimistic euphoria there began what A. J. P. Taylor has called 'the greatest surge of willing patriotism ever recorded'.

At 1 p.m. on August 5, Lord Kitchener, the sixty-four-year-old Field Marshal and hero of Omdurman, accepted Asquith's offer of the post of Secretary for War. He thus became the first soldier on active duty to join the Cabinet since Charles I's reign. Appropriately, it was agreed that his sphere of operations would be military not political. To the public his appointment was an occasion for joy and relief. Now that he was to lead them into war, victory would be assured. To them, Kitchener was an idol: as the *Daily Mail* journalist G. W. Steevens (who reported his deeds) put it, 'inhumanly unerring'. He was the rock of empire, 'more like a machine than a man'. Photographs of him appeared in homes and offices. Restaurants named their dishes after him. The shops were full of Kitchener souvenirs. Day after day crowds gathered to watch him enter and leave his offices, where a mountainous pile of fan-mail was growing. The media adopted him as a figurehead. Like Wellington one hundred years earlier, he would protect them from their enemies. He was the national talisman, the guarantor of victory, and, hoped those who remembered the comparatively few lives lost at Omdurman, victory at an acceptably low cost.

On August 8, two days after taking office, Kitchener made an appeal for 100,000 men to increase the strength of the Regular Army. Volunteers between the ages of nineteen and thirty, they were to enlist for three years or the duration of the war. Before the month was over, this 'first hundred thousand' was safely tucked under the army's blanket, and an appeal for the second hundred thousand (aged up to thirty-five this time) was under way. By mid-September half a million men had enlisted and the flood of recruits was to continue, so that when conscription was introduced early in 1916, the British Army had signed up the extraordinary total of two million volunteer soldiers. '*Kannonenfutter*' (cannon fodder) they scoffed back in Berlin, reading of Kitchener's 'New Army' in the German press.

'Oh, we don't want to lose you, but we think you ought to go,' trilled Phyllis Dare, as Alfred Leete's famous poster of a pointing Kitchener, with underneath the message, 'Your Country Needs You', stared down from the hoardings. Originally a front cover for the popular weekly paper *London Opinion*, the War Office had bought up the copyright within a few hours of its appearance. And now those stern features were everywhere.

Even so, the military authorities were in no way prepared for the 'seething mass' of men – 30,000 a day at the end of August – who answered their call. The queues at the recruiting offices waited for hours, sometimes all night, to gain admittance. New offices were hastily opened: town-halls, libraries, even public baths were commandeered. Recruiting staff worked a sixteen-hour day and slept when they could, often under their desks, while outside the queues still waited. Public school men, university men, bankers, miners, railwaymen and clerks – they enlisted in groups to form their own battalions and platoons. In September 1914 an entire Leeds football team voted to join up together. They chose the Leeds Pals Battalion, one of many raised locally with young men from one area. As recruitment continued, the British Army began to run short of everything but men. There were barracks in England for 175,000 troops and yet Army Reservists alone in August were reporting at the rate of 45,000 a week. The columns of men on their way to tented camps were, few of them, fully uniformed or equipped. They wore cloth caps, bowlers, straw hats; they marched in scoutmaster's shorts. When the khaki ran out, it was replaced by blue Post Office serge, which on wet days, as September drew on, leaked dye down the necks of the troops. Those men who did procure uniforms, faced an embarrassing shortage of trouser buttons.

Inevitably, among so many eager recruits in 1914, there were those who welcomed the call to arms for personal motives. The war presented them with a cast-iron alibi to escape or at least postpone some crisis in their lives. For Julian and Billy Grenfell's cousins, for instance, the inseparable twins Riversdale (Rivy) and Francis Grenfell, the war offered a fresh start as well as a chance to redeem their past mistakes. Uncomplicated, easy-going and kindly but conspicuously lacking education or brains, the Grenfell twins had made many blunders. They came from a famous military family and the Army was their natural home but, being orphans, only Francis, the elder of them, could afford a commission. Rivy, more thoughtful, and always solicitous of his brother's welfare, set himself to earn the money which Francis, the dashing young officer, so carelessly spent. In his efforts to increase their fortune, he tried to cultivate, or at least make himself at ease amongst cleverer men and, rather endearingly, even hired a tutor to teach him history. When he met Raymond Asquith at a house-party, he reported proudly to Francis that he had been introduced to the young man reputed to be the cleverest of their day. 'In the train coming up,' he went on ingenuously, 'while I read four pages of my book he read twenty of his.'

Likeable as Rivy was, he was not mentally equipped to hold his own in the business world. From 1912 some wild speculating and, while the senior partner was ill, a spell at the helm of his city firm, hastened his financial downfall. By May 1914 it was all over. The firm crumbled and the twins lost every penny they had. Their careers, too, had crashed in ruins and even the sacrifice of his beloved polo ponies could not save Rivy from the bitter knowledge that Francis would have to resign his commission.

John Buchan was among those of the Grenfell's friends who tried to salvage something for them from the muddle. By mid-July he had given it up as hopeless. Then, suddenly, on August 4, salvation came. 'What to most people was like the drawing in of a dark curtain,' wrote Buchan, 'was to the Twins an opening of barred doors into daylight.' By joining up, Rivy could atone for his failure. Francis, an experienced officer and needed now, could resume with honour his cherished military profession. Relieved and grateful as they set off to go to war, the twins looked back on August 4 as the day of their personal deliverance by fate.

Rupert Brooke, by contrast, was faced with boredom rather than ruin, and the war, once he had committed himself to it, gave a clear and unequivocal direction to his life for the first and only time. His return in June 1914 from his year-long odyssey through America, Canada and the Pacific islands, had left him dissatisfied and restless. He was torn between a yearning for further travel, and 'extraordinary adventures', and a shamefaced envy of those of his friends who had married and were settling down. To Brooke, this last seemed like a surrender, tame and conventional. And yet, he confided to Cathleen Nesbitt, he was afraid his wanderings would leave him 'washed about'; drifting on 'doubtful currents . . . black waves', or stranded in 'some dingy corner of the tide'. 'You'll be relieved to know that I pray continually,' another letter to his friend Jacques Raverat announced. 'Twelve hours a day that I may, sometime, fall in love with somebody. Twelve hours a day that I may *never* fall in love with anybody. Either alternative seems too Hellish to bear.'

At first, the thought of war seemed hellish too. ('It will be hell to be in it; and Hell to be out of it.') His first thought at the beginning of August was to cross the Channel to France to help gather the harvest. Next, he toyed with the idea of becoming a war correspondent. He had, he wrote to Eileen Wellesley, 'a resentment . . . against becoming a mere part of a machine'. He wanted to use his intelligence. 'I can't help feeling I've got a brain. I thought there *must* be some organising work that demanded intelligence. But, on investigation, there isn't. At least, not for ages.

'I feel so damnably incapable,' he continued. 'I can't fly or drive a car or ride a horse sufficiently well.'

In a few weeks the sight of so many of his friends already in khaki had prompted Brooke to a frenzy of impatient envy. It was Edward Marsh who finally got him his commission in the Royal Naval Volunteer Reserve. Patrick Shaw-Stewart, who had first of all joined the London Volunteer Defence Force, was also helped into the RNVR by Marsh. 'I'm glad I could do it for you, since you wanted it,' Marsh wrote to Rupert Brooke, 'but I feel I'm "giving of my dearest" as the newspapers say. Don't tell a soul that I did it all on my own or I shall be plagued to death.'

By the end of 1914 Brooke and Shaw-Stewart had been drafted into the ill-fated Hood Battalion along with Charles Lister and Arthur (Oc) Asquith, a younger brother of Raymond. After these few short months, Brooke had found in the fighting forces the purpose and simplicity previously lacking in his life. 'The thing God wants of me,' he declared with new-found confidence in November 1914, 'is to get good at beating Germans.' The adventure of war had arrested what he most dreaded, the downhill slide into routine, domesticity and encroaching middle-age. He admitted as much in a letter he wrote in January 1915 to his friend and fellow-poet, John Drinkwater. The war, Brooke decided, was 'rather exhilarating and rather terrible . . . The training is a bloody bore. But on service one has a great feeling of fellowship, and a fine thrill, like nothing else in the world . . . Not a bad time and place to die, Belgium, 1915? . . . Better than coughing out a civilian soul amid bed-clothes and disinfectant and gulping medicines in 1950. The world'll be tame enough after the war, for those that see it . . .'

Few young men greeted the outbreak of war with the belligerent relish displayed by Julian Grenfell. 'It must be wonderful to be in England now,' he wrote home from South Africa at the beginning of August. 'I suppose the excitement is beyond words . . . It reinforces one's . . . belief in the Old Flag and the Mother Country . . . which gets rather shadowy in peace time, don't you think?' For himself, he was 'aching to throw stones at the Germans'. 'It seems too good to be off at last,' he wrote when his regiment finally embarked for France on October 5 1914. 'Everything is perfectly bird.' Once there he told his mother and father that he 'would not be anywhere else for a million pounds and the Queen of Sheba . . . It is all *the* best fun. I have never felt so well, or so happy or enjoyed anything so much. It just suits my stolid health and stolid nerves and barbaric disposition. The fighting-excitement vitalizes everything, every sight and word and action. One loves one's fellow-man so much more when one is bent on killing him.' 'I adore war,' he wrote another time. 'It's like a big picnic without the objectlessness of a picnic. I have never been so well or so happy.' Only those who were close to him like his younger brother, Billy Grenfell, saw the other side – 'the mysticism and idealism, and that strange streak of melancholy which underlay Julian's war-whooping, sun-bathing, fearless exterior'.

His mother saw it, certainly, but refused to recognize it. Etty, impatient, active, inclined to thoughtlessness and insensitivity, was a firm believer in what Cynthia Asquith called 'a stubborn gospel of joy'. Nicholas Mosley, in his interesting and thoughtful biography of Julian analyses this creed, and the effect on Julian up to August 1914 of the conflict between mother and son.

Brought up in an atmosphere of illness and death – her parents, brother and grandmother all died before she was fourteen – Etty protected herself with what Julian's contemporaries christened 'Ettyism': a dogged determination to be happy whatever the circumstances and whatever the cost. As an old woman living on her memories at Panshanger in 1952, she could look back on a life marred by bereavement and grief, and still exclaim brightly: 'We did have such fun, didn't we?'

Julian, always the most sensitive of Etty's children, felt under continual pressure from her unrealistic expectations. Even in her shamelessly euphemistic *Family Journal*, Etty was forced to admit that Julian, since he had gone up to Balliol, was inclined to have 'very vehement discussions [with] his mother . . . not infrequently ending with both disputants in tears. They each held very strong opinions, and could not bear the other not to agree absolutely . . . Julian's mother sometimes felt mildly depressed about these arguments, and used to think how dreadful it would be if anyone ever overheard them and the very plain speaking on both sides; but Julian wholly approved of them, and used to call them his "fight for life" . . .'

At Oxford Julian was a solitary youth and his unsociableness earned his mother's particular disapproval. In letters Etty thrust the gregarious example of her latest lover, young Archie Gordon, at him. 'It's no good trying to improve what you haven't got,' was Julian's retort. 'I'm trying awfully hard . . . with my affectionateness; but either it's not there, or it's got into the hell of a dark corner.' Later, after more in the same vein, he was driven to defend himself more vigorously. 'Did you hurt my feelings?' one letter home asks ironically. 'Not ½. Isn't it a pity I'm so *frightfully* sensitive; life becomes almost unbearable under the strain. However, I actually liked Sunday in spite of the anguish you caused me, and the utterly incoherent and inexpressible workings of my great brain . . . My down is gradually merging into a sort of semi-conscious state with total cessation of all feelings which is rather blissful; I am now on a par with a living sponge, or a polypus, or the higher vegetable world . . .' For all the desperate humour in these sallies, Julian was in real trouble, plagued with an incapacitating nervous crisis. He could not eat. 'I feel such a rabbit,' he told his mother, 'because there's nothing actually wrong with me, only I go on getting more and more dead and miserable and I can't work or do anything.' Mosley points out the connection, which Julian himself may not then have realized, between his listless, semi-starved, apathetic state, and the frequency of Etty's barbs. 'Of course if I have got one (a faculty for affectionateness),' he writes miserably to her on one occasion, 'then the things that you repeat are obviously and doubly true and I'm too bad to live!'

Not surprisingly, it was to his aunt not his mother that Julian went to recover, and thus he missed his twenty-first birthday celebrations at Taplow. Relations with his family had improved during the period of passivity enforced by his illness. '[I'm] only sorry,' he wrote, 'that it [the family] likes me better in depression than elation.' Once his spirits rallied, Julian renewed his 'fight for life'; the struggle to free himself from the choking dependence and conventionality which was the only future his family approved for him. At times he longed futilely to be an artist, but 'it had been tacitly settled from . . . earliest years that Julian was to go into the army,' stated Etty's diary; and even after the loss of two soldier sons, she could still recall with approval how family pressure helped push him into it.

Clear-sighted as he was, Julian could see through the conventional Edwardian wisdom and fashionable philosophy which linked romance with suffering, love with guilt and duty with self-sacrifice; which bound men to women, ensured the dominance over sons by their mothers and required self-immolation as proof of love. He knew, for example, that Etty strove to keep him in her toils by making him feel guilty for any trivial attempt at being different, or at guarding his independence. He could see, too, the hypocrisy latent in the womanly pose she always struck, of joy valiantly transcending suffering. At a time when the rest of the family were sharing 'poor poor darling Mummie's' death-bed vigil by the side of Archie Gordon ('Brave heart,' wrote fifteen-year-old Monica from Germany, 'we *won't* let sorrow creep into our lives, will we?'), Julian was preparing a book which attacked everything his mother stood for.

The book, which was never published, was made up of seven essays. The first, *On Conventionalism*, inveighed against its 'terrible power', which could envelop an impressionable youth 'like a pall, thrown over him by his parents and relations'. Society, the twenty-one-year-old author postulated, did not need 'a fairly good all round man', the sort being produced by the hundred in the Edwardian public schools. 'It wants,' Julian wrote, 'a man who will do one job and do it well.' The lack of individuality, the blind acceptance of received ideas that he saw around him, he blamed squarely on the establishment world, 'the world of etiquette, of manners, of social advancement, its atmosphere . . . the pungent atmosphere of afternoon tea'. This was Etty's world, the atmosphere in which she flourished and, backed up by Patrick Shaw-Stewart who had swiftly replaced Archie Gordon as her current youthful lover, she hastened to defend it.

Julian's work was largely derided or ignored. The family passed it off as a product of his melancholy, written while he was 'temporarily deranged . . . [he] got better the moment it was finished.' Such was the iron grip which convention held on this generation that fifty years later Julian's sister Monica was still dithering uncertainly over the book's merits: 'I wonder if some of it was good?'

Julian reacted to the disapprobation with his severest depression yet, and although he recovered in time, in Italy, the spark of his rebelliously independent spirit seemed finally to have been extinguished. Guilt-stricken, he wrote to his mother for reassurance that 'you no longer think me a perjured and hardened sinner . . . I can hardly imagine *how* sinfully bloody it must have been. I am most *frightfully* sorry and apologetic for it.' By the end of 1910, he was soldiering in India – his choice of regiment, the Royal Dragoons, dictated largely by his desire to leave England for as long as possible. Henceforth, apart from a few relapses when he slipped in references to illnesses and 'nerves', he told Etty mostly what she wanted to hear – that he was 'frightfully well and as strong as two lions'. At any rate, she recorded firmly in her Family Journal that Julian went through no more depressions from this time.

The coming of war in 1914 set the seal on Etty's victory. It kept her son in the army (in 1914 he had talked once again of leaving it) and in a role she could understand and view with maternal pride. Julian, too, must have experienced some relief. Not only was his future now decided for him; for once, he and his mother were fighting on the same side. He died before the mechanised slaughter began in earnest, and while he still had the opportunity to be a gallant individualist. (He 'set an example of light-hearted courage,' commented Billy's Colonel, 'which is famous all through the Army in France.') Given two weeks, after his wounding, in which to prepare herself for his death, Etty faced it the only way she knew how: with dogged and implacable optimism. Julian, she declared defiantly, died 'with the most radiant smile that they had ever seen on his face'.

It is hard to escape the feeling that she had him now where she wanted him: an evergreen hero, hand (in the posthumous portrait she had made) resting protectively on his mother's chair, while she secretly altered his letters to her to make them seem more loving. There were no doubt many others like Julian Grenfell, individualists who saw the dangers – the Great War would horrifically expose them – of strait-jacket conventionality, blind obedience and the cult of the gentleman-amateur. Like him they were alienated from their uncomprehending friends or families. Like him, they became reconciled, first in war, then finally in death.

Patrick Shaw-Stewart had been, in a contemporary's words, 'quite flummoxed' by Julian and his 'profane . . . attack' on their shared world. His social standing was more precarious than Julian's. He had more to strive for and, if *he* offended Society, much more to lose. Yet even he, careerist that he was, confessed to Billy Grenfell the boredom and depression he felt 'at the thought of banking during the dog days and the autumn equinox, and till all the end of time'. 'Poor old Shylock,' commented Billy patronisingly. 'I . . . heartened him with the prospect of being a merchant prince, which is surely as good or better than most things in this untidy and monotonous world.'

Other members of the Coterie were similarly at odds with life in the pre-war world. Charles Lister pronounced dissatisfaction with the Diplomatic Service, which was lonely and boring and which refused to give him the responsibility he craved. Billy himself, in moments of gloom, saw his life as 'a series of shattering disappointments . . . I . . . have a glimpse now and then,' he wrote caustically of his contemporaries at Eton and Oxford who were fast losing the glitter of their gilded youth, 'of what a roaring joke we must present from the bird's-eye point of view.'

The war in August 1914 seemed to offer even these privileged youths and others like them, an exciting chance for travel and adventure. They saw it, many of them, as a welcome diversion from which they would return in time for Christmas, if not before the trees were bare. Meanwhile, they could picture themselves leading cavalry charges against a retreating Hun across the fields of France in crisp, autumnal weather. In this spirit an 11th Hussars cavalry officer, Charles Garrard, even took his hunting-horn and crop with him to the Argonne. 'It seemed like a great adventure,' Ulric Nisbet would record later. 'Everyone was terrifically thrilled . . . That marvellous August of 1914. It was thrilling then for a young man to be alive.' 'Armies, armies, armies,' recalls an old man, once a young officer, in Ronald Blythe's *The View In Winter*. 'We were preoccupied with romantic militarism . . . we talked with shining eyes. I find the world a more peaceful place,' he concluded, 'than when I was young . . . when I went off to fight the Kaiser.'

Ulric Nisbet, a seventeen-year-old schoolboy who had expected to return to Marlborough that autumn, found himself instead one of the first and youngest wartime officers to be commissioned. 'Men lined up as I did outside the local Territorial battalion. We were all amateurs, all the same sort of people. Before the war my father had said to me, "You should go into the Army. You'll get a pension." I said, "I don't like the idea of the Army." But war was different. We were all romantics. We thought it was going to be a wonderful war, full of heroism and glory.

'You have to remember that it was an absolutely steady world. I was shielded by a primal innocence. It was a much more idealistic society. I didn't know anything about the world. I never read newspapers (although I saw the *Daily Graphic* from time to time). We weren't educated that way. With us the attitude was "Theirs not to reason why". There was no tennis at Marlborough, for example. That was too individual: the public school was a team. Games mattered, although always as an amateur. Gentlemen who worked in business for £200 or £300 a year got off to play cricket. I remember Ken Woodroffe, a fellow-cricketer and senior Marlborough prefect, being upset that "soldiering in some capacity" that summer would upset his invitation to play cricket against Lancashire. When he referred to "this blasted war", that's what he meant. As it turned out he was dead by 1915. He was killed in action at Neuve Chapelle.

'Like multitudes of other young men,' Ulric Nisbet wrote of the outbreak of war, 'I became filled with a passionate desire to take part in it. I drank in everything that was written by statesmen, ministers of the Church about the nobility of our ideals and the righteousness of our Cause. It wasn't a matter of "Our Country, right or wrong". Our Country was 100% right and Germany 100% wrong. We were fighting for King and Country and Empire, and "gallant little Belgium". We were fighting to uphold the principles of justice and freedom, and international morality, and to smash Kaiserism and German militarism.' They were not bloodthirsty, Nisbet concludes, 'just blithely unconscious victims of a one-track educational system ... We had been taught to worship God one day a week but to worship Country and Empire seven days a week. The British Empire was the greatest empire the world had ever known, and its greatness was due to the superior qualities of the British.' Anyone who did not think so, and who did not believe in the war was a cad, 'an absolute outsider, deserving of white feathers, ostracism, even imprisonment . . . Looking back,' Ulric Nisbet observes wryly, 'I was good material for an empire-builder. It was a terrible thing but that then was the state of consciousness. You didn't question it. Everyone accepted it. No-one saw anything wrong with it. On the Somme they just died and that was that.'

And so instead of planning for a new term at school, Ulric Nisbet spent the first weeks of August discussing with his father and friends of a similar age how and when to join up. 'Fortunately, the local TF battalion wouldn't have me. They were over-strength with suitable volunteers of nineteen and over already ... It looked as though I should be forced to return to school,' he wrote, 'a project that filled me with despair. However, a little influence and the indispensable Public School connection got me a commission in a

Special Reserve infantry battalion.' He was commissioned on August 15th 1914 – one of the first new officers after the outbreak of war, and at seventeen one of the youngest lieutenants in the Army at that time. With his clothing grant of £50 he procured a sword, a Sam Browne belt and his uniform. He had his sword sharpened for one shilling. At Fagg in St James's Street he paid 'the shattering price of five pounds' for boots. In France they were 'indisputably worth it'. On his Second Lieutenant's pay of 5/6d a day, he bought a two-stroke Calthorpe Junior motorbike. Ulric Nisbet was now ready to begin his military career at Chatham Barracks in Kent.

Ulric Nisbet was in the view of many of his contemporaries lucky to have received a commission so soon. At Kingston Barracks, headquarters of the East Surrey Regiment, an ex-dairyman who had recently taken the King's shilling, was trying on August 4th to hold back the flood of would-be recruits beseiging the main gates. 'There I was all dressed up,' recalls T. A. Silver, 'one of the last in the British Army to be still in scarlet uniform. But that day was the last I saw of my precious scarlet. They were outside the main gates, clamouring to get at the Germans. The Guard Sergeant told me not to let any of them in without papers. They were allowed entry only ten at a time. They got very restive. The pressure was enormous. They tried to force the large iron gates at the side. I lost three scarlet jackets that day. We changed over to khaki overnight.'

For the less fortunate, the miners, dockers, mill-workers, and particularly the unemployed, the rush to the colours represented a serious and pressing need to escape the drudgery or poverty of their daily lives. It is no accident, surely, that the mining and industrial parts of the country recruited proportionately the greatest numbers of men. At a time when the average wage for long hours was £2 a week; when the value of these wages was in decline; when unemployment, particularly in the building trades, flourished; when boys left school at thirteen to labour sixty hours for a five shilling wage, the poor had little enough to look forward to and, it seemed to those volunteering, nothing much to lose. Herded into factories and mills and the evil, cramped tenements which were a legacy from the Industrial Revolution, the simple reality of the good food and fresh air enjoyed by Army recruits was a powerful inducement to them. It is a telling fact that most city-dwellers in the great recruitment wished to join a cavalry regiment. The promise of seeing the sights beyond the nearest street corner attracted others in an age when few people had ventured further than the nearest seaside resort or local town. 'Both my parents were dead,' recalled one such young recruit in 1914, 'I was very poor and had never had a holiday in my life. When I joined up at Nottingham, I refused the local units, and asked which other battalions were open. I chose the Northumberland Fusiliers because it gave me the longest train ride.'

A sense of righteousness softened the edges of these hard practicalities. A natural indignation against the Hun for being the Hun ('patriotic and ignorant . . . patriotic and primitive', a former Fabian calls his 1914 philosophy) was buttressed by the press reports of German atrocities in Belgium. Robert Graves has clearly chronicled the speed with which such rumours spread, citing in chronological order, a sequence of 1914 newspaper reports:

When the fall of Antwerp became known, the church bells were rung [i.e. at Cologne and elsewhere in Germany]. *Kölnische Zeitung*

According to the *Kölnische Zeitung*, the clergy of Antwerp were compelled to ring the church bells when the fortress was taken. *Le Matin*

According to what *The Times* has heard from Cologne, via Paris, the unfortunate Belgian priests who refused to ring the church bells when Antwerp was taken, have been sentenced to hard labour. *Corriere della Sera*

According to information which has reached the *Corriere della Sera* from Cologne, via London, it is confirmed that the barbaric conquerors of Antwerp punished the unfortunate Belgian priests for their heroic refusal to ring the church bells by hanging them as living clappers to the bells with their heads down. *Le Matin*

The five thousand unfortunate civilians who happened to be killed during the 1914 German advance into Belgium, became in the eyes of the opposing press and public, victims of a calculated policy of repression, sacrilege and murder. In just one article the *Daily Mail* on September 22, 1914, managed to revile the Kaiser as a 'lunatic', a 'madman', a 'monster', a 'barbarian', a 'criminal monarch' and a 'modern Judas'. When even an intelligent young man like Robert

Polo at Ranelagh, July 4th 1914.

Above left:
Hilda French aged 15 shortly before the war wearing an ostrich feather hat given to her by Fred Felstead.

Above:
Subaltern C. A. F. Drummond, RFA, in greatcoat and non-regulation balaclava outside 'The Cottage', France, November 1914.

Left:
Pearl Barrington Crake as a 1914 debutante.

Graves considered only twenty per cent of 'the atrocity details' to be 'wartime exaggeration', it is no wonder that others, more impressionable, swallowed the entire catalogue whole.

'Each of them [the 1914 volunteers],' wrote C. E. Montague in his 1922 work *Disenchantment*, 'quite seriously thought of himself as a molecule in the body of a nation that was ... "straining every nerve" to discharge an obligation of honour ... All the air was ringing with rousing assurances. France to be saved, Belgium righted, freedom and civilisation re-won, a sour, soiled, crooked world to be rid of bullies and crooks and reclaimed for straightness, decency, good-nature ...' Newly-fledged privates like Thomas Bickerton of the Royal Sussex Regiment, 'felt that what we were going to do was something that had just got to be done. Had not the Kaiser invaded Belgium and were not the Germans a bad crowd?' Even now among those 1914 recruits still left alive there is an echo down all these years of what they knew as 'the 1914 spirit'. 'Us 1914/15 boys volunteered,' an eighty-four-year-old ex-gunner reminds Ronald Blythe in *The View in Winter*. 'I am glad I went; I'm proud of it . . . I'll say I am! . . . I got cut-up a good bit, but I wouldn't ha' missed it . . . As God's my Maker, I wouldn't ha' missed it, cup-up an' all . . .'

In London Geoffrey Barrington-Chance, an Old Etonian engineering apprentice, saw the results of this patriotic fervour. He himself was stranded without money. 'Fortunately, I knew the Grosvenor Hotel where my parents had stayed for years would cash me some. The queues outside the banks were enormous and no-one would accept a cheque. There was chaos in the streets. I saw dachshunds kicked and *Appenrod* the German sausage shop in the Strand was knocked to pieces by a mob. Already, troops were everywhere. Drafts hustled here and there. I saw a battalion of Guards march past the Grosvenor Hotel through cheering crowds. Other chaps wandering along with an NCO had obviously just enlisted. They were pretty lax about age or medicals. If you wanted to go, you could go.' In this spirit Stanley Patston was accepted into the City of London Rifles 'with a wink and a nod although I was fifteen only on July 5'. When war broke out he was a cadet bugler in the King's Royal Rifle Corps. Immediately, the Colonel in their camp at Shorncliffe called a battalion parade. Many of the cadets were seventeen, he pointed out, and eligible to join the Army. If that was not possible they should volunteer *en bloc* for a regiment in the

TF. 'When he yelled, "Battalion Shun!" . . . Like a lot of twerps we all stepped forward. I knew I could pass as seventeen.'

As a Woolwich cadet in his final term, Cyril Drummond's commission was a foregone conclusion. Nevertheless, it was still a 'thrilling moment' for him when he received the telegram on August 4 requesting his return. No-one at Woolwich, he maintained later, had any anticipation that summer term of European war. But looking back, he could remember from earlier in the summer two prophetic remarks, which, it seemed to him after August 4, had been a warning of what was to come. At a friend's house in London he met a young German. 'Are you Regular or Territorial?' he was asked. His reply of 'Regular' met with the retort: 'Ah, the first that we shall meet.' Shortly afterwards a friend from Sandhurst (an ex-Marlburian who had stood next to Cyril Drummond and the boys from Tonbridge in the Public Schools' Contingent lining the route for the King's Coronation) visited the Mess of the Munster Fusiliers. The general prediction there, he reported to much amazement, was that there would be war with Germany within the next three years.

At the end of July Cyril Drummond had gone home to Norfolk. 'I had a two-stroke Douglas motorbike I'd bought that summer, and both it and I went by train. I had an easy time at home at first. I played tennis a lot at the home of Dr Belding, a GP nearby who had a very beautiful daughter. Afterwards one afternoon we had tea in the drawing-room. Someone said – to me it was the first real suggestion of it – "What bothers me is all this talk of war." Of course the room got going. The elderly lady next to me said, "Of course, they wouldn't send you." "Oh yes," I replied airily. "My term would go out straight away. In the Boer War the senior term were commissioned immediately." She was a bit shaken at that, I thought.'

Now that the recall order had come, Cyril Drummond was determined to obey it promptly. 'We were two miles from the railway halt. It was not a proper station and there was not another train that night. In my eagerness, I put my things in a bag tied to the back of the old Douglas, and saying to my people, "I'll see you when I see you," I chugged out along the road. I thought I'd better go in the direction of London. It was a lovely evening. I was excited and happy and comfortable on my bike. I got to Downham Market and I had to get some petrol. I went to the station which was on a main line to London, and there was a train coming in half an hour. I put my bike in a garage, left my name, and said I'd call for it. Then I bought a ticket to Liverpool Street. The platform was full of chaps, some in uniform, some in plain clothes.

'I walked into the East Lodge at Woolwich at midnight that same evening. Having signed my name, I went straight to look at Battalion Orders. They directed the senior term to take their best dress-jackets to the tailors' shop for the attachment of badges of rank. Next morning after breakfast I reported to the Doctor. The MO and a couple of chaps were in the East Lecture Room taking names. He said to me, "Well, Drummond, are you fit?" "Yes, sir." "What do you want?" he asked. Seeing my chance I said, "Well, sir, I'd like the Field Artillery." "Right-o. We'll put you down. It may not be at once, you understand. You may have to go to the fort for a bit. No trouble at all?" he finished. "No, sir." "Right-o. A1."'

That day, August 5th, Drummond went to a private tailor he knew in Woolwich. He took his sword to be sharpened, and he shopped for some extra 'kit' at the Army and Navy Stores. 'When war broke out I said to myself, well, you've got to think this out for yourself, find out what you've got to do and do it. As an only child I'd learnt you'd got to depend on yourself. When I chugged on my bike again up the Rectory drive, my father was in the garden. I heard him call out, "Mother, here's the boy." It was funny next week waiting for orders. The local people, none of them realised what war would mean to them. No more than I did. They remembered Mafeking – that was a big night even in that little village. Even so, there was a bit of the idea of "Let the squire and the parson send their sons." To which my father could always say, "Well, I've sent mine."'

On August 12th Cyril Drummond's longed-for commission arrived from the Royal Field Artillery. But his first posting seemed an anti-climax and cruelly unglamorous: Maryhill Barracks in Glasgow.

Amongst the Coterie, with the self-professed exception of Julian Grenfell, there had not been wholehearted enthusiasm for the war. On August 4 Diana Manners recalls being with Ego Charteris, Cynthia Asquith's brother, playing, ironically, with tin soldiers on the flagstoned courtyard of a country-house. Alongside them, the older generation harked back nostalgically to their duel with the Boers. 'It'll take a week or two to roll 'em up,' she remembers someone exclaiming with relish. On August 7 Diana Manners had, in forcibly light-hearted vein, written what she called her 'Peace

Letter' to Edward Horner. 'Edward, darling,' it began: 'I think it's up to the Coterie to stop this war. What a justification!' She went on to suggest asking a neutral country to intervene and ban all hostilities until a peace settlement was arranged. 'You mightn't believe it,' she ended sombrely, 'but this is written more seriously than I've ever written. My fears are your own war lust.'

'How I wish you were at the War Office, Dottie,' wrote Raymond Asquith, 'instead of Kitchener. We should all sleep easy in our beds . . .' In another letter dated August 1914 he reported being 'chid this week in London by Nancy Cunard for failing in brio and insouciance and forced to plead guilty to a certain lack of blitheness . . . Certainly in London the fog of war as they call it had got into everybody's lungs, and the air was thick with the feeling that England expects everyone to make a fuss . . .' He himself had put himself down for 'a thing called the London Volunteer Defence Force, organised by Lovat and Desborough, having the following among other advantages a) it is not yet in existence b) the War Office may stop it ever coming into existence c) Patrick [Shaw-Stewart] belongs to it d) no member of it can be called on to perform even the simplest act of duty for several months e) no member of it can possibly be killed till Goodwood 1915 at earliest.' 'If the war is really going to last three years,' he concluded bitterly elsewhere, 'we shall all be under the sod.'

Nevertheless, by 1915 Raymond Asquith was fighting in France, and Patrick Shaw-Stewart was in the trenches at Gallipoli, despite having admitted to Diana Manners when actually faced with donning khaki, 'I am the most unmilitary of men. I hated field-days at Eton. I hate the very thought of taking the field now: I do not particularly dislike the Germans . . . I know full well that although I may be a bad banker I should be a hundred times a worse soldier . . . I frankly recoil from the thought of wounds and death.'

'The only sound thing is to hope the best for one's country and to expect nothing for oneself,' wrote Ego Charteris to his parents. '. . . Write down everyone one loves as dead – and then if any of us are left we shall be surprised. To think of one's country's future and one's own happy past . . . When all is said and done we were a damned good family. I couldn't have had more joy out of anything than I have had from my family . . . Tell Papa he must write his sons off, and concentrate on his grandsons who, thank God, exist.'

Such breathtaking idealism (Ego Charteris was only thirty-two) seems awesome to us now; no theories about war fever, no statistics about unemployment can ever quite explain it. The majority of volunteers in 1914 do seem to have felt as Cyril Asquith claimed of his battalion, in some measure, 'almost as if they were crusaders . . . they felt fulfilment and satisfaction in doing something necessary. They all had something in them of the public spirit. They felt in one way or another that they owed something to society, some gratitude for the good things that life had given them . . .' Certainly, not all of them were swept up by unthinking euphoria. Not all of them believed the war would speed to a quick and glorious end. The bravery of those who feared the worst and still followed the recruit-ing-sergeant seems in the light of what happened to them and how their worst fears were realised, all the more poignant.

Among the bohemians and Bloomsburyites of the Café Royal, barbs, smirks and a great deal of cynicism were the lot of those hotheads who rushed to volunteer. Nevertheless, many did. On the night of August 4th, J. B. Booth who walked in from Piccadilly with Edgar Wallace, found the packed Café in a state of 'dazed excite-ment . . . The incredible was happening, even as one sat there in those utterly familiar surroundings . . . The Chelsea Set, with the usual female appendages, was inclined to boisterousness, but the men from Fleet Street and the theatre world talked in undertones . . . The smoke-laden air was full of rumours . . .' Inside, the German waiters, with an eye for their own self-preservation, had jumped on the marble table-tops and were singing the *Marseillaise*. Outside, the German prostitutes disappeared from their regular beat in Piccadilly, only to reappear with dyed black hair and a smattering of decidedly Teutonic French. Most of them were rounded up for internment in any case. In the next few days, as more and more of its habitués appeared in uniform, the plush scarlet decor of the Café was splashed with sombre khaki. The models cheered as their favourites came in minus their bohemian clothes and their hair. Herbert Read was one who joined up, along with Wyndham Lewis and the 'New Ager' Ashley Dukes. The new Private Dukes, who had on occasion brought Rupert Brooke in to drink at the Café, now found himself banned from the chess table while an officer was playing.

'*We* are the civilization that you are fighting for,' shouted one artist at a group of soldiers. 'We were just beginning to be a little civilised,' declared an outraged Roger Fry shortly before August

4th, 'and now it's all to begin all over again . . . I hoped never to live to see this mad destruction of all that really counts in life . . . Oh if only France would keep out and leave Slavs and Teutons to their infernal race hatreds! But we are all trapped in the net of a heartless bureaucracy!' Later on, the war became 'like living in a bad dream'. Gloomily, Fry struggled to maintain his Omega Workshop, and shut himself up in his studio in Fitzroy Street, its space as always cluttered and untidy, filled with the debris of painting, cooking, sleeping, eating, living. His current works came and went on his easel; the still lifes of flowers, fruit and vegetables remained on his table with a note – 'Do Not Touch' – for the cleaner. But Fry himself felt, he revealed, 'a kind of deadness' to go with his conviction that the war would not, indeed, end that winter. 'Oh the boredom of war,' he wrote even at this early stage. 'The ways of killing men are so monotonous compared to the ways of living.' And his main concern continued to be not victory over the Germans, but French culture, French art, French civilization. Rheims Cathedral he excepted from his list of threatened masterpieces: 'No bombardment can do anything like the damage that the last restoration did.'

D. H. Lawrence, on the other hand, was more concerned for humanity. On the outbreak of war he wrote to Cynthia Asquith that it had finished him. 'It was the spear through the side of all sorrow and hopes.' He saw it as 'the end of democracy, the end of the idea of liberty and freedom, the end of the brotherhood of man, the end of the belief in the reign of love, the end of the belief that man desires peace, harmony, tranquillity, love and loving kindness, the end of Christianity . . . the end, the end, the end'.

At the Morrells' house in Bloomsbury, the news of war had been greeted with similar expressions of shocked outrage. They had returned over the bank holiday weekend from Black Hall, Philip Morrell's family house at Oxford, to find, 'even our quiet Bedford Square filled with bands of youths marching around singing the *Marseillaise* and waving flags'. As Philip Morrell, upset and agitated, rushed to the House of Commons to voice his protest, Ottoline Morrell sat alone on the evening of August 3rd 'waiting and waiting, simply racked with the horror and madness of the war and the utter folly of our joining in'. It was her view that, 'Want of courage and decision on the part of Grey . . . has let the . . . jingoes get the upper hand, and war madness is running wild and will force his hand.' On August 4th, with Bertrand Russell, Ottoline walked the streets, trying to calm her nerves and soothe her anxieties. She arrived at the House of Commons and stood in the outer lobby, observing the reactions of M.P.'s to the approaching crisis with Germany. 'A few ... [were] miserable but the majority flushed and excited.' She noticed one face in particular, 'flushed and happy', and 'marvelled that anyone could look or feel happy at such dire news'. Another call that long day was on Princess Lichnowsky. A small crowd stood outside the German Ambassador's residence in Carlton House Terrace as Ottoline Morrell attempted to make her farewell. 'I called on the house, now shunned, filled with ghosts of the gay people who had swarmed there.' Afterwards, walking up the Haymarket and seeing all the people going about their business, she wanted to shout out a warning to them of how drastically and violently a war would change their lives. Back at Bedford Square a small but determined band of pacifists had already gathered, among them at this early juncture, Granville Barker, Ramsay MacDonald and of course Bertrand Russell. Russell professed himself horrified that ninety per cent of his countrymen were gleefully anticipating bloodshed. He wrote bitterly some time later that having supposed that 'most people liked money better than almost anything else ... I discovered that they liked destruction even better ... I became filled with despairing tenderness towards the young men who were to be slaughtered, and with rage against all the statesmen of Europe. For several weeks I felt that if I should happen to meet Asquith or Grey I should be unable to refrain from murder.' Later, Adrian Stephen, Duncan Grant, Arnold Toynbee and J. M. Keynes would join the Morrell circle, supporting the 'Friends of Foreigners' who gave money to the wives and families of interned German waiters, now 'enemy aliens'.

Mark Hayler, without the benefit of a famous name or influential connections, had only the backing of his family in his determined stance against the war. In his quiet suburban neighbourhood, 'when war happened, it was a thunderbolt. The English weren't expecting it. Looking back in my diary, the first mention of any such catastrophe comes on July 31st.'

On August 4th Mark Hayler was in nearby Croydon, trying to help a group from the Social Reform Congress due to sail that day to Oslo. 'The shipping company, the Wilson Line, were refusing to send out ships, saying, "Who's going to pay if we are torpedoed?" The British government offered to meet the costs. We put as many on board as we could. We wanted as many as possible to try and stop the war. When the boat came back in to the Tyne, they wouldn't let it in. They thought it was an enemy ship. It had to wait outside for hours to go on up and dock.'

Later in the week Mark Hayler saw 'young soldiers marching down the streets, their wives and sisters marching in step behind them. They were going to join the trains en route for their camps. There was no sadness, not a trace of fear. They thought it was a nine-day wonder and would be over in six weeks or so. *No-one* imagined four years.'

Mark himself was 'knocked sideways' by the events of August 4th. 'I didn't know how I would react before. I'd never thought about it. I might not have been much of a pacifist in the event. But as well as a deep conviction I had a general fear of being manhandled. I hated the idea of being knocked about. I hated the idea of violence of any sort.

'I wouldn't join the RAMC because that was mending soldiers only to send them back. I wouldn't even join the Friends Ambulance Service, although it was unofficially Quaker, because it was linked to the military. They didn't carry rifles but they were directed by the Army. When all our efforts to stop the war failed, I joined Fenner Brockway in the No Conscription Fellowship. The Church was very bitter about CO's [Conscientious Objectors] like me. They thought they were disgraceful. The man in the street was very bitter. People on buses would look at you. They knew. Your age would give you away. They came right out with it: "Why aren't you in the Army?" The hostility was very noticeable. I just tried to think of my friends and my hope that they understood. And after all, if you've burnt your boats, you can do anything. You're free then. You're free from the inner things that imprison people. Even when conscription came in and I would say to my family and friends before I went out, "If I don't come back, I might have been arrested," I wasn't afraid. A police-man or recruiting sergeant could easily stop you and ask you for your papers. If they thought you were evading the draft, they could take you straight back to barracks. Even then I could have claimed exemption or asked for an office job. But I didn't. That would have released someone else.'

For Hilda French in domestic service in nearby Kingston, the date August 4th had long held a singificance of its own quite apart from the war. 'Fred, my young man, worked as a steward on the

Union Castle boats. He was due to sail on August 5th. On August 4th we went up to London. We couldn't afford the train fares so I'd never been before. Waterloo was packed with soldiers. We went off to the zoo. He said as we went round, "I've got something to tell you, dear. I'm sailing on the *Galway Castle* in the morning." I said, "Will you be all right?" He said, "Oh, yes, the war won't touch us." Well, they got to South Africa. As they were going into a port, they could see flames and smoke. It was a German cruiser. Another ship had her boilers out and was shelled in pieces. The *Galway Castle* thought it was all right to go in. The cruiser had scooted off. They ended up being turned into a hospital ship and kept in port. We got letters saying he was delayed. Finally, they got home, him and his brother and my sister's boyfriend. They all said, "Oh, let's go and join up and have a bit of fun. It won't last long." He had leave to come and say goodbye. My mistress gave me a day off for us to spend together. In those days it was unheard of. He bought me a little ring and said, "Keep it till I come back." I asked, "Could I have a week off? It's his last leave before going to be a soldier." She said, "Oh, no." I thought – that's it. I can go on to ammunition. I gave a month's notice. She said, "You can't go. We shan't get another one. They're all going into munitions." But I was sixteen and I knew this courting was serious, so I said, "I regret this, but . . ." I went out of domestic service saying, "Hoorah!" I went home to find my brother had joined up so I could have the downstairs bed-sit.

'My sister was in the same position. She worked for some jumped-up, toffee-nosed types, the sort who bragged, "We can afford a maid." In the afternoons she had to get dressed up in a black frock with apron and mob-cap. One afternoon they said to her, "Nellie, go and post the letters." My sister started taking off her cap and apron. The lady said, "Why?" She said, "I'm not going up the road like that." "Oh, yes, you are." "No," she said, "I'm not. Not any longer." And she gave a month's notice too. We both went to work in munitions. I worked in a factory in Kingston building the first aeroplanes. I got £5 a week. I thought I was it.'

The First World War dealt a major blow to the whole domestic service edifice. Hundreds of grooms, gardeners, chauffeurs and stable-boys joined up. Thousands of working-class girls put away their mops and floor-cloths and went to work in munitions factories. Indeed, despite the inconvenience, it was deemed unpatriotic to prevent them, and Jennie Churchill took to the pages of the daily press, urging that all male servants should be encouraged to enlist. Society must learn to do without their footmen so that their footmen could do their duty. Lady Randolph herself had been inspired by the splendid example set by Walden, her late husband's manservant. Over-age but determined nevertheless 'to go', Walden asked Winston Churchill to use his influence for him. Before long Walden was at the War Office, no doubt in a coveted job, 'looking immaculate in military uniform', decided his employer, 'as he escorted officers to various departments'. Jennie Churchill, it must be said, did not intend to be left short of staff by his departure. To fill his position she engaged two parlour maids whom she dressed in Tudor costume. Later on, she had her footmen's liveries re-cut to fit round their female contours.

The staff of the aristocracy, whose greater numbers probably ensured an easier workload, and whose sense of status was often buttressed by the consciousness of serving a great titled name, may have had less to lose by choosing to remain in domestic service despite the alternative occupations offered to women by the outbreak of war. In middle-class homes one or two maids-of-all-work were frequently expected to turn their hands to all the domestic chores. Yet their employers spurned such drudgery-saving implements as gas-cookers or the new portable vacuum-cleaners (first introduced in 1910), preferring to depend on their maids for a constant supply of cheap, tireless labour. No wonder girls like Hilda French, considered not quite educated enough to serve in shops or wait in tea-shops, saw in the munitions factories, despite their gruelling schedule, a last chance to achieve respectable independence. That they were well-paid was for many merely a delightful bonus. To escape from domestic service was enough.

Only in 1919, when in many a home what Lady Bunting (writing in the 1910 *Contemporary Review*) had deemed unthinkable had happened ('No one to cook the dinner, answer the door, attend to the children, and carry out the many other requirements of an ordinary household'), did public interest grow in new domestic gadgets. The magazine *Homes and Gardens* which came into being in June 1919 turned its attention immediately to everything from galvanised mop-buckets to the first American dishwasher. Henceforth, everything would be designed around what they named the 'daily-help' home.

Violet Graham's family had been otter-hunting as August began.

'That was the big event, not what was happening in Europe. We felt justified in killing otters because they ate salmon. My cousin was staying and we bicycled to where the hounds met and then followed on foot. My mother came later with the lunch in a hired wagonette. Early in the morning on August 5, we were in the garden playing tennis behind the high garden wall. We heard the troops from the nearby Territorial camp march past down the road. We thought nothing of it – they did march occasionally. But they were singing *Tipperary*. It was the first time we heard it. We went to the front gate to see if they had gone. A van passed. It had a placard on its back: "England Declares War on Germany."

'People went off very fast. The first one was a naval officer on leave. A boy who came otter-hunting with us went off to be a spotter in the Royal Flying Corps. My brother at sixteen was in a great stew. He thought he wouldn't be old enough, and when he was, no one would be able to afford to continue the war.'

On August 6 1914 in London, *The Times* reported that six thousand Americans had arrived from the Continent. They had embarked, 'scores of them' the writer said, in crowded boats at Calais, many of them with no luggage and only the clothes they had on. In the White Room at the Savoy Hotel the American Relief Committee set up their headquarters, learning to their relief that White Star and Cunard Lines were to resume their sailings across the Atlantic within forty-eight hours. The American Luncheon Club and other long-term American residents in London had set up the Relief Committee within twelve hours of the war declaration. Their resources were stretched from the start as telegrams, letters, messages and enquiries after missing persons piled up; while their distraught and penniless countrymen badgered them for passages home and funds. A rule was applied by the Relief Committee that they would cash forty dollars per person. Meanwhile, British hotels, railways and shipping lines accepted travellers' cheques and letters of credit. More substantial help was on its way. For 80,000 dollars twelve Americans bought the 8500-ton steamship *Viking*. She sailed from Liverpool a week after war was declared with four hundred passengers under the American flag. The minimum fare was one hundred dollars, the maximum twenty-five dollars more. Passage on a second steamer was being arranged for those with no ready cash at all.

The American cruiser *Tennessee* was reported to be sailing from

New York with a cargo in gold of several million dollars. The Pennsylvanian Railway Company cabled five thousand dollars, and on August 7th a notice posted in the Savoy informed the hapless Americans that Congress had voted 2,500,000 dollars for their relief. The Savoy Hotel attempted to help by offering simpler, cheaper dinners at a special sitting in the main restaurant from seven till nine p.m. It was especially generous at a time when they had lost so many staff, seventy German and Italian waiters alone having returned to their country's colours.

Meanwhile, the daily scene in the great white and gold ballroom of the Savoy was, reported the *Daily Graphic*, 'like a co-operative American town. The women are in smart and serviceable tailor-mades and the men in baggy, comfortable-looking clothes – completed by soft, felt hats tilted far back on the head, and to complete the typically American picture there is the iced-water table stationed at every entrance.'

Despite the *Daily Graphic*'s sartorial scorn, the Committee, considering the confused circumstances, was by now working most efficiently. A messenger service was provided for them by the Boy Scouts. Stranded travellers arriving at the main railway termini were directed promptly to the Savoy. The Committee gave advice on banking, finance, postage, transport and lost luggage. One member had already set out with a single courier for Germany in an attempt to trace twenty thousand lost American suitcases. By August 15th an American newspaper had indexed the names of twelve to fourteen thousand refugees, estimating that two thousand more were added to the list every day. 'My daughter Olive Maddox,' ran a typical item on the Lost and Found Bulletin Board, 'is alone in London. Can probably be found through Thomas Cook ... or engage police. Please find her and arrange return. E. L. Maddox, Grand Rapids, Michigan.'

Bidding for steerage passages to New York soared to unheard-of prices. American doctors, nurses and governesses plied their trades in an attempt to work their passage home. The new four-page *American Bulletin*, however, counselled sensible delay. Its advice was pitched deliberately low-key and reassuring:

> Don't worry – to do so is to annoy yourself and, what is more important, others.
>
> Don't forget you have no monopoly of troubles.

Don't forget rural England is a most beautiful place to spend August in, and that you always wanted to see it.

Don't grab a state-room for four when there are but two in your party.

Don't forget that there are others just as human as you who want to get home too.

Pearl Barrington Crake was in the meantime filled with anxiety for her aunt who was stranded in Germany. 'At the end of the Season my Uncle Lionel Dugdale went off to Scotland and Aunt Vi took a cure at Wiesbaden. When he heard that war was imminent, he wired her and she got into the train and got as far as Freiburg. There they took all the luggage out of the train and the whole station was piled top to toe with their luggage. She arrived back on August 4th after a most appalling journey. They had no baggage, nothing to eat. She was only allowed to keep her handbag. She had been foolish enough to take all her jewellery with her, and she arrived home without a stitch and everything gone. For the rest of the four years she always hoped and hoped that she might have got something back. In the Foreign Office they said, "Don't worry," and they were absolutely marvellous. But she got nothing back.

'Over the weekend my uncle was in such a state. He rang up and said, "Pearl, come down and play croquet or something with me." We went down to Hurlingham, and I shall never forget the croquet. Everyone was trying to imagine what was going to happen. As he spoke to them my uncle got more and more agitated. It was too awful.'

On August 4th Pearl Barrington Crake's grandfather went to work as usual to the City, where the offices had remained open. The Army and Navy Stores where Pearl wanted to shop had closed. Her eighteen-year-old cousin John arrived home without warning from OTC camp at Aldershot. 'Instead of coming home on Thursday, they were all sent off this morning in Specials. The Eton boys were sent home at a moment's notice from Eton, where they'd just got their money to go straight to camp. They were forbidden even to wire, so all the families had their children turning up unexpectedly.'

In the evening came 'a telephone call to say that Aunt Vi had finally arrived safely. Jama, her maid, came round and borrowed blouses and dresses and nightdresses. We all went round to Claridge's to dine with her and hear about the awful journey. None of them thought they would be allowed to cross that frontier. She's never been so frightened. Their joy was untold when they got on to the boat at Flushing, even though they stayed tied to the quayside from 1 a.m. till 7 a.m. The crowds were appalling, people paying five marks for a mat to sit on. Cheques or even banknotes were not accepted. They were absolutely starving. People travelling from Basle or Frankfurt said the Germans took every bit of luggage from the trains as they went through.'

That night 'Uncle Lionel, Aunt Vi and my cousin Tom went to the country. My mother and I went to Charing Cross to see if there were any troops moving. The crowds in Trafalgar Square! And down from Whitehall to Parliament – just huge. All walking up and down, up and down, not knowing yet what would happen.' The next day, when their fears had been realized, Pearl and two aunts who had hastened back from their Scottish holiday, went to Heads in Sloane Street to buy khaki-coloured wool. "We were going to make balaclava helmets for the soldiers to wear at night. *The Morning Post* had said we must all do it. No-one quite knew what we were in for, you see. We all felt we had to do something and fast. I mean, all my family were Army and Navy. But no-one knew what anyone else was doing. We all rather drifted around aimlessly at first, having lunch and tea with each other.' All over the country Relief Committees and Red Cross Nursing Classes had started within a week of the war. There was enthusiasm – at the British Red Cross Headquarters in Devonshire House piles of flannelette waiting to be sewn reached almost to the ceiling – but few able to direct it.

Pearl Barrington Crake's own nursing career started when she went with a group of friends to her first Red Cross lecture. 'It was taken by Sir James Cadleigh, the big and very famous doctor, and held in Eaton Square. He said: "When you're nursing somebody, you must never have a pin on you." He said to me – he was very Scotch – "M'dear, you've got to be a braw nurse." Of course, after that for ever, when anyone came near the ward, I said, "Have you got a pin on you?" This was it. This was my first lesson on nursing. We had bandaging classes afterwards. I was sure I would be hopeless. I hadn't done anything like this before.'

Diana Manners too, in the face of vehement opposition from her mother – who 'hated the sordid, unvirginal aspect of [nursing] and the loss of authority and protection' – was eager to become a VAD. Her romantic idea was to follow the troops to France along with the Red Cross hospitals and dressing-stations being prepared by the

Duchess of Sutherland and others. This earned her mother's violent disapprobation and a plea that she would have no peace for fear of Diana being raped. The mercy mission to France had therefore to be postponed indefinitely.

Up in Derbyshire over the bank holiday before war was declared, Osbert Sitwell was languishing unhappily with his parents, his sister Edith and brother, Sacheverell. On July 20 1914, just as he was beginning to enjoy life as an army officer, his dictatorial father had enforced an abrupt change of plans. Osbert was to leave his regiment, which was far too expensive, and enter the more financially lucrative field of commerce. He would start in a job his father had procured for him in Scarborough as a town-clerk. Each day at Renishaw, therefore, (his father's Derbyshire home), a bowler-hatted instructor from Clark's Commercial College came to teach him calligraphy. Humiliated, resentful of his father's tyranny, angered by his extravagant schemes for rock-pools and garden terraces, Osbert felt, nevertheless, a certain composure. He had friends who liked and believed in him. 'At last [I] felt entirely in tune with my epoch.' As August approached, he claimed afterwards, he did not know what destiny held for him but he believed his future did not lie in Scarborough Town Hall.

On August 2nd 1914, as Sitwell has graphically described, a hot, still, dusty summer morning, his father strolled as usual to the site of an island pavilion he was 'running up' on the lake. Climbing on to the wooden scaffolding with his air-cushion and binoculars, he proceeded to open *The Times*. 'What was that? War! War! There would not be a war; how could there be? The Germans could not afford it and we certainly could not.' As Osbert continued to try to work, his vague and saintly Aunt Florence drifted within his earshot. '*War? War?* The only war she knew was the great and never-ending battle between Good and Evil.' Stunned by what he had heard, Osbert Sitwell for once defied his father, gave up work and walked and talked with his brother. 'Within a day,' he realized, 'the feeling of tension ... had inexplicably and intolerably increased. Yesterday had been an ordinary day, with a threat of worry: whereas today was two days – or a day or three days – before the Great War.'

But when Osbert Sitwell managed, without his father's knowledge, to put a trunk call through to London, he was told by a fellow-officer that 'the scare ... [was] off.' Nevertheless, his battalion had been moved into the Tower at short notice. At six a.m.

on August 4th Osbert Sitwell arrived in London to find a Reserve Battalion being formed. From that time on, he 'lived perpetually on the edge of departure', expecting to be sent to the Front at any moment any day. Among his brother-officers copies of *Old Moore's Almanack* circulated, and visits to fortune-tellers were booked. Osbert, attending one on his friends' instigation, was relieved to hear that he would return from the war safely and become a writer. He was heartened too to hear Sir Edward Grey predict the financial collapse of Germany and therefore the end of the war before three months' of fighting had elapsed. But the hysteria and rumours spread even to Renishaw where Sacheverell remained convinced that 'they saw the Russians pass through the station here last night ... Miss Vasalt telephoned to Mother this afternoon, and said trains in great numbers had passed through Grantham station all day with the blinds down. So there must, I think, be some truth in it, don't you?'

At Belvoir (Diana Manners remembers), the Russians were also supposed to have been seen in the neighbourhood, recognizable to the excited villagers by the snow which still, despite the hot English weather, somehow clung to their boots. Writing to Diana, Raymond Asquith was sardonic about the calibre of some of those who had volunteered to serve in the national emergency. Describing a visit to 'the most amusing place', the National Service League, he mocked 'the vast swarm of well-meaning and inefficient patriots ... employed for fourteen hours a day in first classifying and then rejecting the applications of a still vaster swarm of still more well-meaning and inefficient patriots for posts which they are obviously incapable of filling ...' Nor did his own family escape his sarcasm. From Mells he wrote, 'The atmosphere here is appalling. The crisis has brought out all that is best in British womanhood ... K. [Katharine] still keeps her head but C. [Cynthia] and her Ladyship have sunk all their political differences and are facing the enemy as one man ... They have cornered all the petrol, sold all [the] hunters, knocked off two courses at dinner and turned my child's pony-cart into an ambulance ...'

Such was the zeal of the Masters of Hounds and others whom the War Office had appointed Remount Purchasing Officers, that horses were commandeered sometimes straight from the shafts of wagons making deliveries in the streets. For Cecil Aldin, attempting to find his quota for the cavalry, the first weeks of August contained very long days and little sleep. His fellow Purchasing Officer, to whom he had wired for help when war broke out, refused to interrupt the annual routine of his Scottish holiday. Cecil Aldin was left alone to deal with the complaints of outraged horse owners who saw their precious hunters summarily removed from their stables. On the other hand, scores of brand new cavalry officers pleaded with him for mounts that were 'frisky'. For these would-be heroes Cecil Aldin retained a 'bucking bronco' to dampen their enthusiasm. Other soldiers needed to be taught how to care for their horses, which, unlike their motors, could not run indefinitely. With no male grooms and up to five hundred horses in his charge, Aldin took on women helpers strictly 'as an experiment'. Sceptical at first, he was soon full of admiration for the 'slight little things . . . so small they found it impossible to groom without having buckets or boxes to stand on'. There were other female horse enthusiasts sceptical of the selective skill exercised by some Remount Officers. In Stroud in Gloucestershire Gabrielle West passed the railway-yard, 'which had become a sort of horse-fair. A very young officer was buying remounts. An old coachman told me, "He thinks that lot will make cavalry horses. Them's two-year-old shires. They will break down in a month if they're put to hard work now."'

As a friend of the Squire's wife ('Old Sir William told me most solemnly, "We must all practise the utmost economy now – no more almond macaroons for tea"'), Gabrielle West was drawn into the feverish activity of the local Red Cross. 'Lectures by the local doctors; first-aid demonstrations; bandage-making – it was non-stop. Then the whole detachment was ordered to go to a huge empty house nearby and prepare it as a possible hospital. It was terribly dirty and had no mod. cons. – just one large coal-range. There was not even a hot-water supply. We cleaned it up thoroughly and left the thirty beds ready. It stood vacant for weeks and weeks until one day in the autumn when a telegram arrived: "Fifty wounded will arrive at 4 p.m."'

As the month drew on many large country homes were cleaned and renovated for use as hospitals. Many more were not. Although their owners had, in response to an appeal by the Duke of Sutherland, offered them to the nation in its time of need, there was, according to the *Tatler*, one great drawback. It seemed that 'some of the finest in our old country seats . . . [were] lamentably lacking in that very first essential not only of a hospital but of the most ordinary residence, proper drains . . .' As a result, many aristocratic castles were turned down by the War Office in favour of more comfortable middle-class homes.

Some individuals did not give up easily. Guy Slater has described the single-handed effort made by his sixty-three-year-old grand-father Lieutenant-Colonel Borton, who on August 7th had already measured up a warehouse on his Kentish estate, which he planned to turn into a hospital with twelve beds. By August 12th a special order for these beds was winging its way by post to Harrods. When he was not organising the hospital, Colonel Borton was taking his cowman, his footman, even his forty-three-year-old butler to Maidstone Barracks to enlist. On August 18th, when the news of the British Expeditionary Force's exploits in France finally came to light in the Colonel's breakfast newspapers, his diary reported: 'Put up the beds in the hospital so we shall be ready when wanted.' A few weeks later – his wife having put the final touches to it by staining the cupboards – his warehouse hospital was complete and awaiting inspection by a government architect. As autumn came the nurses were recruited and the beds finally occupied – with four wounded Belgians brought back by the Colonel from Maidstone.

In Gloucestershire Gabrielle West joined the 'feverish activity of the Stroud Red Cross – lectures by local doctors, First Aid demon-strations, bandage-making. Suddenly all detachments were ordered to go to Standish, a huge, empty house and prepare it as a possible hospital. It was terribly dirty with no mod cons, just one large coal range and no hot water supply. Still, we cleaned it up. We were getting used to hard work. Ernest, our own garden boy had suddenly left. We heard from the postman later he had had his medical and gone straight off to Bristol. We were left to dig potatoes, sift cinders, clean our own boots and do half a hundred horrid little jobs we never knew existed. My diary for August 20th lists them all and ends wearily, 'Am beginning to feel as if there really was a war on.' But there were no wounded soldiers in Standish House. Not for weeks and weeks. So we whitewashed and scrubbed our stables, went to Stroud station and commandeered some Belgian refugees. We had to do something.'

As an insignificant servant in an undistinguished country par-sonage, Bessie Ellis's role in the war was even more passive. Her life was at first relatively untouched by it. Irish by birth, she had no relatives in the army. She had no sweetheart to be concerned for either: 'My young man, who came from Pembury, did not go to the Front till 1916. He came back then dirty, shaking with nerves, with only the clothes he stood up in. I never could get keen on the war, seeing what it did to him and to Mr Sassoon.

'Before the war we young people went to each others' houses. The fathers were very strict and most of us went to bed around dusk. But we had a laugh, we played cards or Pope Joan. You had cider and sandwiches and a light supper or biscuits. When the war came, we would hardly go out at all. There was always someone in mourning in the cottages then.

'Oh, they made a big fuss of it. When it came in 1914 we had badges to put on our coats and we had our favourite generals. There were parades and Lord Roberts was always trying to persuade the young men to go. Plenty did round about. They made it hard for them if they didn't. We had much more work to do as it turned out, but it wasn't that so much. I felt sorry for them. Most of them didn't come back, did they? I was never that keen on the war right from the start.'

In Glasgow Cyril Drummond had by this time found himself in a gloomy artillery barracks facing a big barracks square. 'We were a Reserve Brigade. We had horses, gunners, drivers but no guns.' Almost as soon as he arrived he left, dispatched 'to clear up the barracks at Tipperary. The battery there had gone from Ireland at very short notice, leaving behind six young soldiers and a bombardier with a hernia. I lodged very pleasantly with an Anglican padre and spent the entire week, while the chaps were cleaning up, sorting out the correspondence and paying bills out of battery funds. It rained all the time.

'On Sunday I took the young soldiers to church all dressed up in their blues. After the service I stood with the padre's wife and watched one hundred Nationalist volunteers parade in plainclothes. That evening a telegram arrived, ordering me to report back with the detail to Glasgow, wiring ahead my arrangements. I procured a "Bradshaw" and worked out the trains to Dublin, from where we could get a boat. On the day of departure I was up at six cycling on the padre's bicycle to the station. I got there ten minutes before the train was due and the stationmaster held it up for twenty minutes while the lads struggled in with their kit. At Dublin we were met with another set of orders which entirely countermanded mine. I was to go to another quay at 7.30 and meet Mosham, an officer shepherding seventy Special Reservists from Waterford. My boys and I had a bit of a sit down and a bit of refreshment. Then we marched right across Dublin to the docks, with old Irish women pushing bottles of whisky at us and shouting, "Kill the bloody Germans!" At the quay was a small ship. It being Ireland, an MO was coming before it sailed to search for liquor and put a picket on the gangway. At 7.30 on the dot Mosham and his Reservists turned up. He had been marching them about the square at Waterford for hours to get them sober. Even then our troubles were not over. Directly opposite the ship was a pub. The head of Mosham's column marched up the gangway; the tail disappeared into the pub. We spent half an hour fetching them out one by one and pushing them on board. Then he and I took it in turns to stay on deck and keep the party clean. Their trick was to sling water-bottles down the side on to the quay where they were caught and filled. "What have you got in there?" I said to one. His mate nudged him and he replied, "Water," looking at me with saucer eyes. I poured it over the side and as it bubbled out I said, "That's good water." He said, "You might be sorry for that, sir." I said, "So might you." All the while the crowd on the quayside were singing their heads off – *Pack up Your Troubles* and *Tipperary*. I never heard *Tipperary* sung in France while I was there.

'We got back to Glasgow early on Sunday morning. Everything was shut. It was shocking. There were no trams. We had to march from Glasgow Central Station to Maryhill. It seemed like miles. Every night at Maryhill they brought in two hundred civilians who had enlisted. We had nowhere for them. They spent the night in a riding-school. Then next day a subaltern was detailed to take them off. The first lot I took (when I was almost as raw and inexperienced as them) were due to go to Preston. They all formed up and were pushed into line on the barracks square by NCO's. I had a nominal roll but it was pretty chaotic. When we were ready to go I shouted "Fours Right", and they shuffled up and the NCO's pushed them round. We quick-marched to the station where the train was already waiting for us in a siding. I had thought in my innocence that when I gave the order to entrain, the chaps would get in in an orderly fashion. In fact, there was a wild halloo and they piled into the carriages and out the other side, some of them. I went down the train with the bombardier and found three chaps in one compartment, sixteen crushed into another. Someone was wandering around looking for his friend Jock. As the train puffed out they started singing in extempore harmony. It was marvellous. I sat alone and listened in my first-class carriage. As it got dark we pulled into Carlisle. It was a very long platform and we puffed in and stopped just opposite the refreshment room. Before you could say "Jackson", every door was open and every chap popped out. I was distraught as none of them were in uniform and they looked like all the other chaps in the station. I enlisted the Guard's help and got him to blow his whistle five times before the train was due to start. When he did, the doors of the refreshment room flew open, and everyone surged back on the train.

'At Preston we went to the barracks by tram car. I travelled on the footplate of the leading tram with the driver. I handed the men over. There were one hundred and fifty to two hundred of them and only four chaps to control them. The next lot went to Sheffield. We had to march through the town to a hill-top barracks. When we did the roll, I discovered we'd gained one marching through Sheffield. It was quite possible, as there was always a certain amount of chat.

'They were grand chaps, a cheery lot and as keen as mustard. They were practically all Public School and first-class officer material, yet they were put in the line of infantry battalions, serving in the ranks. To see these chaps in the HAC [Honourable Artillery Company], Artists Rifles and London Rifle Brigade change guard was like watching the Guards themselves. They weren't used as they should have been. They were decimated at Hooge. One of the NCO's in the Artists Rifles was married to a cousin of mine. His brother was also a sergeant. I met them at Bayeux when I had just arrived in France and was sleeping on the station platform. Later when we were in the line I hacked over and had tea with them in the back room of a ruined house. In that room we were on a pre-war level and it was "Frank", "Morris", "Cyril". When I said, "I'd better get back now," they said, "Goodnight, sir," and sprang to attention.

'In France many of my fellow-officers had been in the Special Reserve Royal Artillery, and had come into the Regular Army on the outbreak of war. They were far better than I was. They knew far more about handling men and about the duties of a battery officer. The same went for officers who came on from university. They could talk intelligently and had much wider vision. A lot of them had some sort of knowledge of human nature and had met different sorts of men. At Woolwich – the Shop – you were with the same sort of chaps you'd always been with. You'd been with them in the Army

Class at your public school; from there you went to Woolwich or Sandhurst; from there you passed out with them into your regiment. You never talked shop in the Mess. It was an unwritten law. It amazed me later in the war to hear young officers discuss what had gone wrong with an exercise and how they could put it right. Of course, they learnt from it, but it was a thing we never did. You could talk about horses; you could talk about your men, the funny things they said and so on, but you didn't discuss the mechanics of the job. It was the amateur approach that got us into trouble. When the war broke out you could still hear officers like the one who is supposed to have said when his artillery was off target: "Cock her up a bit, Johnnie."'

Ulric Nisbet remembers himself at this early stage in the war as similarly 'quite incompetent ... I was seventeen and a quarter, parading around with a sword and not knowing a damn thing about it.' A few years grudging OTC at school had not begun to prepare him for the duties of a serving officer. Fortunately, when he reached Chatham Barracks where he was to begin training with ninety other young newly-commissioned officers, he found most of them 'almost as ignorant as myself'.

'So much had to be improvised in those early days. We were all to a greater or lesser degree, amateurs. We were not yet cogs in a vast machine but individuals.' In charge of the young subalterns was Captain Wilde: 'We thought he was pretty aged. He used to sleep with his mouth open in Mess. We filled it with paper balls. It was a summer of marvellous weather, 1914, and it was marvellous to be alive. Everything was different and thrilling and far bigger than oneself ... I read a paper-covered book about a club-footed Germany spy.'

They trained hard – 'It was pretty hard work' – beginning with a physical workout before breakfast. Every morning three and a half hours were spent on the Barracks Square with sergeant-majors drilling them in squads. A talk on some such theme as discipline or fire control preceded lunch and then more time on the parade ground. The summer evenings were given over to such visual training as judging distances. In a few weeks Second Lieutenant Nisbet was considered proficient enough to act as the day's Orderly Officer, to hold inspections and take a squad in musketry drill. That, at seventeen, he accepted the responsibility so blithely does not now amaze him. 'It was quite easy. We were the people who built the

Empire. If the war hadn't come, I was going to go out East. If you went to public school you were made for that sort of thing. We were simply following the system taught us. We weren't an elite. We were just educated as such. A public school man was educated to be a leader without really realizing it. We didn't have any class feeling. I had never before met the lower orders. You didn't discuss whether you were a gentleman or not. You just knew, like you knew that at Sussex County Cricket Ground there were two pavilions, one for Gentlemen and one for Players. We were brought up one way, they another.

'The thing was that old lags from the Egyptian War of 1882 would accept this as did the other men. Because I was friendly and proficient enough, they respected me as their platoon commander.' By this time, Nisbet was with his battalion at Fort Darland, just outside Chatham.

'In the evenings we went to the Chatham Empire or Barnard's Music Hall. For more intellectual fare, there was the theatre. At Barnard's, a real haunt of the proletariat, we lowered gifts from our boxes to young ladies who caught our fancy. Clearly these sexually orientated adventures of ours were limited by Public School inhibitions. We younger officers also decamped to London for similar relaxation whenever we could wangle a pass. There was much latitude in off-duty hours at this time.'

In their barracks and makeshift training camps, the volunteer soldiers burned with impatience to reach the Front. 'Everyone,' wrote C. E. Montague in *Disenchantment*, 'had within him the hope of approaching the far-off, longed-for ideal ... the passport to France.' In the second and third weeks of August the new recruits heard that a British Expeditionary Force, 110,000 strong, drawn from the Regular Army, had crossed to Maubeuge in France. Helen Cecil, whose brother George was a friend of their country neighbour, John Kipling, was among the crowds at Waterloo who saw the troops off. 'It all happened so quickly. I was staying with Rudyard Kipling's family when war broke out. My brother George was in the Grenadier Guards in the Regular Army. The next thing I knew was that on August 13th George was due to leave to fight. We tried to keep to the daily routine before he went, nothing special, except that on his last full day with us we took a long taxi ride round London. We talked of houses and the distances he marched and one thing and another. We didn't actually say goodbye. We did give him some little presents to take with him. But even on the morning he went he would not say goodbye. "Au revoir," was what he said. "Au revoir."

'As the time came he got too restless to stay quiet, and once again he drove about with Mummy and me in a cab. We went to the station to see him off with a basket of pears and a basket of plums for him. I rubbed noses with him instead of a kiss. It was our usual salutation. There was tremendous excitement all around – heads sticking out of all the windows and people pushing food hampers in. I gave George a New Testament. As we ran beside the train, the band struck up "God Save the King".

'I think he knew what he was in for but if anyone ever suggested he wouldn't go, his face fell. He was killed almost immediately. His body, which was missing for a long time, was found on September 1st, his eighteenth birthday.'

Pearl Barrington Crake also spent this time saying goodbye to her friends and relations who were going to France with the Army. 'My uncle Dick,' read her diary for mid-August, 'goes out with one of the first lots. He isn't allowed to say where. We only know that he sleeps in Southampton tonight. Poor Sissy, his wife, came with him to say goodbye. She's frightfully plucky.'

A few days later Pearl Barrington Crake's brother-in-law crossed the Channel with a battalion of the Coldstream Guards. Then came the hardest farewell: 'Dick Lumley (one of my young men) telephoned from Aldershot that his regiment, the 11th Hussars had gone already. He was quite heartbroken because as junior ensign he had been left behind to bring out a consignment of horses. He's on his own down there and wants to come up to London and spend the day with us tomorrow.' The next day her diary reported that, 'Dick Lumley arrived just before lunch at one o'clock. He's taken a box at the Hippodrome this evening. He says we have cheered him up. The poor old boy is very depressed, although he tried to be jolly. We found it difficult to keep off the war topic. He's so longing to go and frightfully excited. We are really the last people he will see in England and we all said goodbye to him. They came at 9.15 for him to motor back to Aldershot. We all sent him off with every good luck.

'He was one of my young men, you see. He was eighteen like me. How many evenings we'd have them all coming in and they'd take us to theatres and then we'd say goodbye to them.' Dick Lumley's death followed almost immediately. Then a few days later Pearl recorded in her diary that, 'Frank Tyler from the 15th Hussars is dead. He was staying with Aunt Fanny for the Wells' dance at Newbury only five weeks ago. It all seems such a short time ago. It seems unbelievable that all this is happening.'

On August 21st Pearl and her mother went to a service of intercession at St Paul's Church in Knightsbridge. 'There was a marvellous sermon, but that awful hymn – "swept their sons away" and that sort of thing – and there we were in floods of tears. Not long afterwards my mother instituted the rule which we followed every single, solitary morning of not opening the papers until we'd had breakfast. You see, every single morning we looked through that ghastly list and there they were, all our boyfriends, killed, wounded or missing. The first list came through after the Battle of Mons after several days without news. After that it went on and on. All my friends were killed. You cannot imagine what it was like.

'They used to have seventy-two hour leaves. It was the most marvellous thing in the world. They were suddenly given leave and they left the Front and put on all their best clothes for London. They wore white ties and white waistcoats and took their young ladies to the theatre, and you did as much as you could, and in seventy-two hours they went straight back. You didn't talk about it or what it was like. What I did was go to Fortnum and Mason and buy them hampers. I remember the great Hugh Cubbitt – I was engaged to him briefly – whom I used to send Elva plums. I used to imagine him opening them in the middle of some awful ditch somewhere. Anyway, ten days after I saw him off, he was dead.

'Everybody had lunch and tea with each other to try to occupy ourselves. Gladys, my sister and I, used to go down to Weybridge where a great friend of ours, Leila Barlow-Webb, was Quarter-master of the VAD detachment. We were on the domestic staff of a big convalescent home which was to be turned into a hospital. We'd never never never worked so hard in our lives before. We got up at half-past five and washed and laid up for nine meals a day: two breakfasts, two lunches, two teas, two suppers in the evening and elevenses. We were still in our teens and we'd never worked like that in our lives. My two aunts, one aged seventy and the other seventy-five, were meanwhile working in the Officers Families Fund at 29 Berkeley Square. The parcels poured in to the enormous hall of this lovely house, and my aunt's job was to unpack them all and gauge

[153]

their condition. At odd moments when I was around I worked there too and so did my mother.'

On August 29 *The Times* late war edition was, noted Pearl in her diary that night, 'too appalling. In the accounts of the war in France, they say whole British regiments are simply cut to pieces. Hardly a man remains and those scattered everywhere. Losses are supposed to be great, but not a list of any sort has arrived as yet. The anxiety of the families!'

From Belvoir Diana Manners wrote sadly too. 'We are all dispersed – my brother to the Derbyshire Territorials, Ego [her brother-in-law] to the Gloucestershire Yeomanry. I was left to comfort my weeping mother who was losing her only son, to toss around some late Midland hay, and to think of schemes to stop the war.' As summer ended she returned to London and Guy's Hospital on a grey and miserable day. A few nurses shivering in their cotton dresses were hurriedly crossing the open courtyard with its Dickensian arcaded passageways. When Diana Manners pressed a side-bell, the door was opened to her by an aged housekeeper dressed in a white hospital cap. From now on, in an 'absurd cap', black shoes and stockings, a floor-length pin-striped dress and an apron 'cut to deform the figure', Diana Manners helped to nurse civilian patients and thus free others to tend the wounded. Transformed from her exquisitely-dressed pre-war self, she hated her appearance: 'Indeed I did look horrible.' She hated too the contact with cancer cases and appendicitis which were to turn her into a hypochondriac for the rest of her life.

As autumn drew on, the first convoys of wounded arrived at hospitals all over the country. They arrived often at night, the stretchers handled gingerly by elderly civilian orderlies. They arrived and their cargo of exhausted, frightened, damaged men – of head wounds, stomach wounds, amputations, tetanus and gangrene – were handed over to the care of young girls totally unprepared for them. 'We'd believed there would be plenty of trained nurses to guide us,' one VAD explains, a vicar's daughter from the west country. 'In fact, I had a ward of twenty-eight beds entirely to myself. It was a baptism of blood. Imagine if I'd been younger, eighteen, and faced with this. I'd done the First Aid and Home Nursing exam. I wanted to do a job. But I never dreamed it would be anything like this.'

6

The Elizabethans

VIOLET GRAHAM became a nurse too. In pre-war days, unlike most of the VAD's, she had passed her Red Cross exams. The experience did not stand her in good stead. 'All I can remember is a local doctor interviewing me and being taught to carve a chicken and make beds.' There were more bed-making and bandaging classes when war broke out, but there were no wounded soldiers to profit from all this hectic if misguided instruction. 'I hung around waiting for a hospital to be opened near us, then I began to bicycle up the hill to serve the troops in the camp canteen. Eventually I joined a hospital in Bath. The first day we VAD's arrived, an Australian was heard to ask, "Which are the ladies and which are the proper nurses?" The man in the next bed replied, "Shut up, you fool. The ladies are the ones with crosses on their aprons." The trained nurses were not too pleased, but the Tommies had never seen VAD's before and they were fearfully impressed. They kept saying, "Do you know, Nurse, that one's a general's wife, and she's a bishop's daughter."

'The hospital trains, known as "convoys", came in mostly at night. They glided in so quietly, very very softly with no bumping. It was very moving. They were so brave, those boys. And so grateful to be out of the war for a while.'

Hilda French's Fred had no such respite from the trenches but he managed to survive all four years unscathed. 'He had several close shaves. At Ypres their own shells dropped on to the British trenches. The communication wires were broken. He volunteered to re-establish them and got stuck in a shell-hole for three days up to his neck in mud. He was with an officer. The officer was given the Military Cross simply for coming back with his head on his shoulders. Fred got the Military Medal presented by Earl Haig on the battlefield of Ypres, but that was after four years of it – the Somme,

Ypres, Passchendaele. He was at them all and he was still under twenty. Those are meant to be the best years of your life.

'We had a great Armistice, though. Then afterwards the penny dropped. I thought, "What am I celebrating? I haven't heard for a fortnight. Something must have happened to Fred." He used to write to me regularly, you see. A whole lot would arrive by the sackful together. He would do things like pick two beech leaves as he went up the line, and write "Keep these, dear. I'll tell you about them when I get home." I could read between the lines. That was his way of saying he might not come back. He never spoke about it otherwise.

'Some weeks later at the factory they said, "There's someone outside wants to see you." He was there in civilian clothes. His teeth had gone bad. He said, "Ooh, my teeth." I said, "Never mind about your teeth. I've got you."

'After the war I expected to hoot at the so-called ladies having to do things for themselves. But we were thrown out of the factories with nothing. It was the same for us as it was for the soldiers. In 1919 Fred went down the Labour Exchange and I went back to work in domestic service. Things had changed a bit. I went back on *my* conditions. I got all Sunday and one half-day off a week, and they let him come in the evenings. But I never wanted it. It was a great come-down. I worked for sixty-seven years after that.'

After Hugh Cubbitt died, Pearl Barrington Crake went to her aunt in Yorkshire. 'Their home, Crathorne Hall, was turned into a convalescent home. She never had a uniform off her. I worked on the staff there for quite a long time. Every day was the same awful routine.

'My brother-in-law arrived back from France in a hospital ship in September. He went to Sister Agnes's home for officers in Grosvenor Place. He was shot by a bullet right across the temple artery. His old servant Brorows clapped a field-dressing on him and that absolutely saved his life. He had very bad concussion and couldn't remember anything. They had to stop him getting excited and keep him very quiet. The pathetic thing was that we didn't want him to get well too quickly or he'd only have to go back to that dreadful place. The bullet landed in his haversack. He kept it and was very proud of it. My sister had it covered with silver afterwards and wore it always, hanging round her neck.'

Ulric Nisbet was also saved by a providential wound. But as he waited in 1914 to cross to France, such thoughts were far from his mind. 'I remember gazing with fascination at some wounded soldiers in a sunny playing-field at Brighton (where my parents lived) and realizing that they had actually fought the Germans at Mons. One's only aim was to get out there before the whole thing ended.'

Nisbet's 'baptism' took place on the Somme. He arrived there on August 26 1916. The day afterwards on August 27, he saw his first dead German. 'He was lying, as though asleep, in a shallow hollow, his face with slightly pointed moustache, mahogany brown, almost black from exposure. Older than I, peaceful and innocuous. I thought, "Why should he have been killed? What have we against him?"'

Ulric Nisbet had no further chance for a while for such unwarlike reflections. He was wounded by a whizz-bang – 'as we called the fifteen or eighteen pound shells' – one day later and, hit in the arm and leg, wandered through the lines for five terrifying, disorientating hours until he regained the safety of his trench.

On February 3 1917 after convalescing in Devon, he left England once more for the sector of the line at Givenchy where the trenches were in some places only twenty-five yards apart. One month later, while observing the German lines from a sap through a periscope, he was sniped in the shoulder. His wound was a life-saving one, coming as it did the afternoon before he was due for a night patrol. The directions to find the German sap were written on a small buff envelope. They read: 'From 1 Sap to keep on left of first knife rests. Carry on in front of them to small boulder, turn sharp left and work up to peak, then path gradually twists to left about fifty yards.' 'How,' asks Ulric Nisbet rhetorically, 'could these instructions have been followed on a pitch dark night and within yards of the enemy?'

Mark Hayler did not reach France until after the war in 1919. He went then voluntarily, to work in an aid programme which fed the hungry and helped in the rebuilding of homes. He lived in Paris and then in Berlin, feeding destitute students in the German capital. The years before he had spent, after a court-martial for evading military service, in jail in England. 'The policeman came up our garden path. I saw him. I was standing where it was light by the window, drawing a map showing where there had been a restriction on alcohol in the world. My father invited him in. I said, "This is nearly finished. Can't you wait until tomorrow?" He was adamant. I suppose he thought I'd run away.

'I was the first man arrested in Croydon and the first to be court-martialled at Aldershot. I was held at Prince Consort Barracks. There were hundreds of soldiers there, and no-one to understand, no support. My family were wonderful though. My father got the press to my trial. They printed a whole page of my evidence (I didn't have a solicitor) in the *Aldershot News*. My father got 1000 copies printed and distributed one to every MP.

'It was hard in jail but the hardest part – standing up and being counted – was over. I went to France to do *my* bit when the war was over. I was in Versailles when peace was signed.'

Cyril Drummond had been longing to do his bit ever since war broke out on August 4. He was 'more thrilled and excited than I had ever been' when he finally sailed for France. 'I went down to Southampton and there was a boat there called *Rowanmere*. I asked a deckhand on it to show me to my cabin. He said, "What are you, a general?" I said, somewhat abashed, "No, a subaltern." There were three thousand on board that ship. You couldn't throw a biscuit very far.'

Cyril Drummond arrived in France in November 1914. The enemy was quiescent but there was enough to contend with in the mud and rats. Despite sump-pits and duckboards, 'the mud was everywhere . . . in some communication trenches so deep and viscous that an ordinary gumboot could be sucked off your feet as you ploughed your way along.' In his sector there was one particularly ferocious rat, 'enormous . . . with venomous eyes . . . He could walk on top of the mud into which I sank at every step . . . I freely admit I flattened myself against the trench wall and let him go past . . .'

In July 1915 Drummond's regiment was ordered to Beaumont Hamel on the Somme. From March 1916 onwards he was in training for the 'Push' which 'we all hoped would lead to a general advance on a wide front and the end of trench warfare . . . We now knew [it] was an exciting possibility.'

On June 30, the evening before the battle, 'before dusk I rode forward over the ground I would have to cross, and down into the dead ground behind the trenches.' Assuming the attack was successful, he would pass through here and deep into No Man's Land to give support fire to the victorious British advance. But meanwhile, 'it was a quiet, peaceful evening and war seemed far away. Our own guns were going, of course, but there was no enemy response, and even close to the trenches everything seemed relaxed and outwardly calm. On the ground beside a pile of boxes lay the body of a soldier who had been killed earlier in the day. He was covered by a blanket, but one corner was awry, exposing an arm, torn, shattered and dirty. Suddenly, for the first time, the thought crossed my mind, "Shall I be looking like that this time tomorrow?"'

In fact, when July 1st came it was for Drummond, waiting behind the lines, a day of 'frustrated inaction, waiting hour after hour for the hoped-for order [to advance] which never came. News filtered through from time to time . . . it was all terrible . . . For some days after the abortive assault . . . the ground between the opposing trenches was dotted with tiny points of light. These were reflections from small triangles of bright tin which each infantry soldier had worn stitched to the small pack on his back, and they indicated where men, dead or alive, lay where they had fallen.

'One day, perhaps a week after the first attack . . . word came through . . . that at a specified time white flags would be hoisted at points of our front line and doctors and stretcher parties would go out under the protection of the Red Cross and try to bring back any living wounded they could find. I was to hold the Battery in readiness to open fire if there was any offensive action by the Germans.

'When the time came, our white flags duly went up and immediately, it seemed to me, three lines of German trenches stood up, each one full of men, looking across at us. Then, when the stretcher parties went out, a number of Germans came out too from their side to meet our doctors and lead them to where they believed men were lying still alive. I believe quite a number were brought in that day but it must have been a terrible ordeal for them lying out there day after day badly wounded and with little if any hope of rescue.'

By the end of July Cyril Drummond was out of the terrible battle which still raged on the Somme. He was wounded, not disablingly but seriously enough to be taken to the Military Hospital in Boulogne. 'From then on I was out of the war. A Queen Alexandra's Nursing Sister – she was Irish – tucked me up in bed and murmured softly, "Ah, you had someone's prayers." She must have been right . . . But on each July 1 I lift a silent glass to all the friends who were with me that day in 1916 and who did not come back.'

Cyril Drummond's friends who perished on the Somme,

Kitchener's volunteer army of 1914, Diana Manners' dashing young men who died one by one, walked down the dusty lanes of France and into legend. Those who did not return from the Great War became part of 1914's legendary lost generation, the gilded youth without whom no golden summer would be complete. The innocent flower of the nation crystallized in perpetual youth: the boy heroes, strong and clever and brave. High or low, plain or handsome, exceptional or ordinary, the young volunteers of 1914 have been transformed by legend into so many Rupert Brookes, blond like him and like the knights in the Victorian paintings still familiar in 1914 to the middle-aged population. Years later the disillusioned and disenchanted could still draw refreshment from the memory of their sacrifice and the thought that the lambs who went to slaughter were so pure, so blameless.

How soon this process of transfiguration began can be seen from the sort of letters which poured in to parents like Willy and Etty Desborough in the summer of 1915 when, in the space of just over two months, they lost both Julian and Billy, two of their three sons, in the trenches. Julian's death especially evoked a nationwide response. The day after he died on May 27 *The Times* published his poem 'Into Battle' which he had sent back to his mother from the front line in April 1915. It was immediately taken to heart by *The Times* readers for which they deemed its qualities of youthful serenity and acceptance. 'And he is dead who will not fight,' wrote Julian Grenfell, 'And who dies fighting has increase.' 'The fighting man,' he continues, will 'find, when fighting shall be done, Great rest, and fullness . . .' 'Nor lead nor steel' will 'reach him, so/That it be not the Destined Will.'

Such seeming calm resignation to the imminence of danger and the possibility of death went some way towards assuaging the guilt felt in great measure by the older generation. Countless strangers wrote to Lord and Lady Desborough after the publication of 'Into Battle', requesting information about the young poet. Bewildered, Julian's father reacted like the honest, straightforward but essentially unimaginative man he was. His son, he protested, 'did not look on himself as a poet, but as . . . a fighting man, boxer, steeplechase rider and lover of animals . . . He used to write verses when the spirit moved him and very often throw them away . . .' Nevertheless, it is not surprising that Julian's poems evoked such an immediate and country-wide response. Over and over again in the letters which Etty

Vehicles, private and commercial, being commandeered by the
British Army in Hyde Park, August 5th 1914.

Cartoon in *Punch*, August 19th 1914.

Hilda French (extreme left) as a munitions worker, 1915.

Mark Hayler (seated second from left) among Conscientious Objectors in Dartmoor Prison, 1917.

Desborough must have read and answered, the writers turn themselves inside out in their efforts to be seen to share the dangers, experience the pain that their sons were going through. Unwholesome intimations of sacrifice creep in. 'None of us who give our sons in this war are so much to be pitied,' writes Lord Grey, 'as those who have no sons to give.' Continues Frances Balfour, 'There is something very wonderful in motherhood today; we have given our children . . . and it is given to us to know that what we have given of ourselves has done its duty.' 'How truly the English aristocracy has proved itself in these past and glorious days,' boasts Katherine Tynan Hinkson while another friend assures Etty, 'They were indeed your "jewels" and you have given them.'

Above all, these parents and uncles and aunts and friends were concerned to blot out any suspicion of waste, to step back from any untimely doubts that their beloved had not died the most gallant and easiest of deaths in the noblest of causes. Before the Somme and so early in to a long and bloody war, this delusion was not too hard to maintain. Thus, Walter Raleigh could write, apparently sincerely, to the mother of Julian and Billy: 'I have only one longing – that my son may enter the Navy next year and be ready to lay down his life as yours laid theirs down.' While the diplomat, novelist and linguist Maurice Baring, admittedly fulsome in his tributes, claimed death for the young soldiers as 'a privilege and a prize beyond anything . . . dreamed [of] before the war. To say it is a waste is to me like saying the frankincense, gold and myrrh of the Three Kings was a waste.'

Bloodthirsty and hypocritical as this sounds to us now looking back on the savage reality of life, and death, on the Western Front, the older generation then gulped down such bromides only too readily, and continued to do so, even after the huge losses at the Somme and Passchendaele. Blinkered to the reality of conditions in France, only a small minority on the Home Front shared the growing scepticism and demoralisation felt amongst the troops, and voiced in late 1916 and 1917 by such young officers and poets as Wilfred Owen and Siegfried Sassoon. 'What passing bells for those who die as cattle?' demanded Owen savagely, while for Sassoon there were 'dreams that drip with murder'. A year earlier and only shortly before he himself was killed, the young ex-public schoolboy poet Charles Sorley had bitterly concluded that:

Such, such is Death; no triumph, no defeat
    Only an empty pail, a slate rubbed clean . . .

But back in England among Etty Desborough's circle, her response to the loss of her sons in 1915 was regarded as a landmark in patriotic motherhood. No mourning, she decreed. Instead, she put oak leaves on Julian's grave in the military cemetery near Boulogne, and entering in her diary a day-to-day record of his two weeks in hospital there, wrote: 'The thought that he was dying seemed to go and come but he always looked radiantly happy and he never saw any of the people he loved look sad.' Billy, writing to a friend at Oxford in the two short months that were left to him, added: 'I love to think that [Julian] has attained that perfection and fullness of life for which he sought so untiringly. I seem to hear him cheering me on in moments of stress . . . There is no-one whose victory over the grave can be more complete.' A memoir published in 1919 and based on Etty's privately printed *Pages from a Family Journal*, a memorial to Julian and Billy, echoed Billy's words and applied them also to his own death leading a charge on July 30. 'None doubted,' the author ended his tribute, 'that no more complete victory over death than theirs had ever yet been won!'

Victory over death. This was one illusion which served as balm to the grief of bereaved parents. They clung to the idea of death in battle as chivalrous, beautiful, the culmination and crowning experience of a young life. Their attitude betrays the widespread ignorance among those at home about conditions in France. The troops did not talk of it; the newspapers did not publish the truth about it. The closest many Londoners got to experiencing 'the Front' was to walk through a dry, deep, neatly sandbagged exhibition-trench dug for the curious to inspect in Kensington Gardens. Mud, blood and mutilation were unthinkable, or at any rate best not thought of. Nor was the death-dealing role of machines understandable to a generation who still liked to believe in war in terms of cavalry charges and knightly hand-to-hand combat. Those who were killed became, defiantly, more beautiful in death, enshrined forever in their youth and poised, like Rupert Brooke's young men in his poem *1914*:

    With hand made sure, clear eye and sharpened power,
    To turn, as swimmers into cleanness leaping . . .

Thus, the author of a tribute to John Manners, Diana's distant cousin, who was killed at the age of twenty-two in the first month of the war, chose to look backwards for his inspiration to brighter days. By recalling John's speed and strength on the games-field, he revived memories (consciously no doubt) amongst the stricken family and their friends, of the triumphant innings at an Eton v. Harrow cricket match which ended John's schooldays in a blaze of glory only a few years before. The image summoned up is one of carefree youth at play, testing out their stamina and athleticism on the playing-fields of England before the team goes out to 'play the Great Game', as Sapper has it in the Bulldog Drummond books, on some wider, foreign field. The poem was originally in Latin. Billy Grenfell, John Manners' friend and real-tennis partner, translated it.

> O heart-and-soul and careless played
>   Our little band of brothers,
> And never recked the time would come
>   To change our games for others.
> It's joy for those who played with you
>   To picture now what grace
> Was in your mind and single heart
>   And in your radiant face.
> Your light-foot strength by flood and field
>   For England keener glowed;
> To whatsoever things are fair
>   We know through you the road;
> Nor is our grief the less thereby;
>   O swift and strong and dear, Good-bye.

As a regular soldier who had joined the Grenadier Guards some eight months earlier, John Manners was the first of his particular group of friends to go to France, the first to see action and the first to be killed – in his case during the debacle of the Regular Army's rout from Mons. It was this group, the 'little band of brothers' Billy Grenfell wrote about, whose early promise and violent early deaths gave substance to the idea, which gained ground after the war, that an exceptional generation had grown up and perished, leaving behind them a gaping void in English life.

In 1916 Raymond Asquith was shot leading his men over the trench parapet during the Battle of the Somme. His son inherited Mells when Edward Horner, the last of a four hundred year-old line, was killed the following year. Edward, Katharine's brother, had been conspicuously handsome, sociable and extravagant, though not gifted with the intelligence the rest of his family took for granted. His third impulse when war was declared (the first had been to ignore it; the second to apply for a commission) had been to order a special pair of riding-boots in which to enter Berlin. Now he was dead, and his death left his friend Duff Cooper reeling. After John Manners' death in September 1914, Edward and Duff had drawn much closer. This second loss gave Duff the conviction that there was little or nothing left to live for. 'The dance is over,' he wrote sadly in his diary in 1917, '. . . it is time to go.'

In fact, the dance of death was not over yet. In 1917 Patrick Shaw-Stewart, too, was mown down. Unlike Charles Lister who, 'bleeding like a pig', was wounded three times before he died of his wounds in August 1915, Shaw-Stewart had survived Gallipoli only to perish two years later in France. Back home in England, Duff Cooper absorbed this fresh blow 'unutterably sad'. By managing to survive until 1917, Patrick had been 'almost the last' of his friends to stay alive. Despite his inward mood of despair, Duff Cooper himself survived, although like many survivors he never quite shook off his feelings of guilt for having done so. Years later when he was Viscount Norwich and could count amongst his attainments a spell as British Ambassador in Paris, he still displayed, most noticeably in his autobiography published in 1953, a preoccupation with those of his circle, 'the bravest, the noblest and the best', who seemed most fitted to live but who nonetheless had perished in the Great War.

Duff Cooper and his friends were an elite, and they were clearly conscious of the fact. 'That haloed band,' Diana Manners could say, referring to her own small, exclusive circle, 'who were to die in the war and leave us *our generation and England* woebegone and maimed'. Nevertheless, there was a need among them, and it is an understandable one particularly in those who faced death themselves, to make each death add up to something more than a headstone in 'some corner of a foreign field', followed by swift consignment to oblivion. And so, each loss of life had to assume especial importance, not just to family and friends but to the shadowy masses out in the English countryside who might have benefited from the existence of such a man, cut down so cruelly before his prime. Thus, Billy and Julian Grenfell, two amiable young men, assumed on their deaths the proportions of '. . . glorious beings . . . shaded between the

Greek demi-god and the young Roman Emperor'. 'It is easy to idealize Julian,' Raymond Asquith wrote. 'One might have set him up in a public place as a heroic or symbolic figure of Youth and Force.' Patrick Shaw-Stewart went further: 'His physical splendour was so great . . . He was the most magnificent human being I have ever seen.' To Charles Lister the loss was more grievous still. 'He stood for something very precious – for an England made of honest, brave and tender men . . .' Henry James was being proved right more quickly than he knew when he wrote to console Etty Desborough on Julian's death, '. . . out of his sublime young image, a noble and exquisite legend will flower.'

When his turn came to die, Raymond Asquith received the same sort of exaggerated adulation. An acknowledged wit, he became to Maurice Baring, '. . . the wittiest man I have ever known; his wit was like a shining icicle . . .' 'Many gave their all for the cause,' eulogised John Buchan, 'but few had so much to give.' Asquith was a 'scholar of the ripe Elizabethan type, a brilliant wit, an accomplished poet, a sound lawyer . . . Debonair and brilliant and brave', he was now 'part of that immortal England'.

Elizabethan – the choice of word is significant. Along with the Greeks and Romans (John Manners, like the Grenfells, was considered to have 'whipped the Greeks into a top hat' for 'beauty, temperance, vigour and reserve'), it was to the Elizabethans that these dead youths were often to be compared. *The New Elizabethans* one book written in 1919 called them.

Cynthia Asquith attributed the tag to a tribute paid to Charles Lister by Sir Rennell Rodd, the Ambassador under whom he served in Rome. Lister, his Ambassador wrote, 'combined . . . the spirit of the sportsman . . . with the instincts of a scholar gentleman'. His love of adventure was of the sort found in those 'large-horizoned Elizabethan days'. Kindred spirit to Sidney and Raleigh, he would have been 'welcomed at the Mermaid Tavern'. This nonsense was quickly taken up and applied by some to a wider cross-section of soldiers, indeed to 'every class and vocation . . . all ranks in the new army'. As a description of the fighting forces, dead, wounded or thankful to be alive, it fitted in with everything the post-war population wanted to believe about their liberators, who were supposed to have greeted war as a great and glorious opportunity in which to display their Elizabethan patriotism and buccaneering Elizabethan spirit.

Cynthia Asquith, while she could recognize the origin of the term 'New Elizabethan', and in a book described the growth of this 'legend', fell prey to another aspect of it. From her pre-war stance as a critic of the Coterie, tut-tutting primly at their unwholesome cynicism, the deaths of so many of them in the war provoked a radical change in her attitude. 'The dazzle of their wit and fancy,' she decided, 'concealed their underlying earnestness.' She added more disingenuously: 'To their contemporaries their bright flippancy was never more than a quite transparent veil.' To Cynthia Asquith all these young men became in retrospect, 'brilliant scholars ... athletes ... poets'. Nor was she alone in this self-deception. G. K. Chesterton, who at forty was too old to be a combatant, wrote of the army in the 1914–18 war, 'One does not know if it is fighters singing, or singers fighting,' thus adding to the false impression that every poor bloody infantryman was also a gifted poet.

The speed with which the legend of the New Elizabethans took root and flourished, suggests that it fell upon fertile ground. Indeed, it was widely held, in books, in articles, among the writers and memoirists of the Thirties and Forties, that it was the best and brightest among Britain's youth who had flocked to be slaughtered on the front line, thus depriving her of her future leaders, and condemning her to be a nation of the second-rate. We find this spelled out in contemporary magazines like *The Nation*, which in 1930 published an article on the theme that the lost generation had few survivors, and that those who had come through, were not to be found in the mainstream of public life. Compton Mackenzie, the novelist, who was one of the Great War generation, took the view that the Second War's outbreak could be linked directly to his countrymen's experiences in the field twenty years before, because 'the loss of the flower of our youth' left 'too many careerists in politics'. Reginald Pound, who himself volunteered to fight in 1914, called his book written in 1964, *The Lost Generation*. Its thesis was that the Great War had led to 'impoverishment at all levels . . . There was no estimating the extent to which creative thought was depleted, or the cost to learning, literature and science of so many strong and cultivated intelligences.' (Heresy even to hint that it took bad luck rather than any lofty attributes of mind and soul to get in the way of a whizz-bang.) It was left to the robust, unsentimental intelligence of Robert Graves to point out that 'the men who had fallen . . . were not particularly virtuous . . . but just average soldiers.' Even this unrevolutionary statement shocked his local vicar and the congregation who had turned out to hear him.

Graves was speaking at a memorial service shortly after the war, so that the frosty incredulity which greeted his breezy admonition that they should all 'thank God they were alive, and do their best to avoid wars in future', is understandable. But the cult of the dead was to linger for an unhealthy number of years. This, and the image subsequently conjured up of a leaderless society poised on the abyss, was used to excuse the way things had turned out by those who could not come to terms with the post-war world of strikes and unions and bureaucracy and a shrinking empire. It was easy to blame the dead, to exaggerate their virtues, squandered in the mud of Flanders, to re-write history in terms of 'what might have been'. Indeed, in the confusing new world which the war had helped to create, the dead were the safest and most convenient section of the population *to* blame, for what was seen as the continuing decline of England.

For there is no doubt that for the middle and upper classes, the war had led to the ground of a whole civilization, once thought solid and immovable, being shaken up in the most violent social upheaval in modern times. When the smoke cleared from the battlefields, it was a new landscape they saw before them: one with which, bruised and battered as they were, they were ill-equipped to deal.

There is nothing mythical about the dangers faced and losses suffered by junior officers in the First World War, who shared the dangerous and dirty life in the line with their troops, and whose perilous responsibility it was to mount raids (cutting the enemy's wire or repairing their own) and lead attacks. Army records show losses amongst British officers to have been significantly higher proportionately than those of the troops, and with the senior ranks comfortably dug-in well to the rear, it was on the young lieutenants and captains that the bullets rained. Particularly at the beginning of the war, when losses were gravest and a young officer's life expectancy at the front shortest, it was the sons of the aristocracy and upper-middle classes who died in proportionately the greatest numbers. Fresh from public school and university, they had flocked in August 1914, to answer the call of the recruiting-sergeant. Being generally healthy, well-fed, tall (the required height was 5′ 6″, raised to stem the flow of recruits in September 1914 and then hastily reduced, ultimately to 5′ 3″) and easily spared from their civilian occupations, they were grist to the army's mill. Those who could not pull strings and wangle a commission joined up as privates, notably in the Honourable Artillery Company.

The result was what E. S. Turner called 'a squandering of blue blood . . . In the first year of war forty-seven eldest sons of peers died of battle wounds. By the end more aristocrats had been killed than in the Wars of the Roses.' The deaths among Oxbridge graduates were one and a half times the army average: a number approximating to three years' intake of students died from Christ Church, Oxford, alone. Of the eight scholars and exhibitioners who went up to Balliol with Harold Macmillan in 1912, only he and one other were still alive in 1918. After it was all over, he could not bear to return and finish his degree. To him, Oxford seemed now like 'a city of ghosts'.

Poems, memoirs, privately-printed remembrances, recollections in school and college magazines – the surviving elite set to work resolutely to perpetuate the memory of their dead brothers, sons and schoolfellows. The myth of the 'lost generation' is a testament to the success with which they did so. Gradually, the word 'lost' – at first used to describe the young men who, having spent their youth in the trenches, emerged after four years of war emotionally scarred and disorientated – was being transmuted into a suggestion of physical loss, of huge gaps in British regiments, families, clubs and workplaces. 'Ghosts of a time no future can restore,' wrote Vera Brittain of her generation of survivors, 'we desolately roam forevermore an empty shore.' The implication was that there were few of them left: the reality was very different. British losses in the Great War added up to 37,000 officers, 700,000 men, a huge and sobering number to be true, but hardly a majority of the males born between 1882 and 1901 who were of call-up age between 1914 and 1918, and five million of whom were still alive in 1921. France lost approximately twice as many men – 90,000 dead or wounded in the first six months of the Verdun campaign alone. In England, it is an inescapable fact that most of those who fought returned.

Nevertheless, the legend proved more powerful than the statistics. 'The unreturning army that was youth,' mourned Siegfried Sassoon in 1918. 'Each week we sent out thousands that returned by hundreds,' accused John Peale Bishop, while his lesser-known contemporary F. S. Flint wrote in a poem that it was as if 'the young men of the world' had been 'condemned to death . . . The growing, the ripening fruit . . . torn from their branches.' The idea of an entire, brilliant generation, poised on the brink of manhood, grow-ing up only to become machine-gun fodder, has proved to be one of the most potent and indestructable of the myths surrounding 1914.

Never Such Innocence

TWO POLARIZED MYTHS are enshrined in the canon of myths about 1914 Britain. In one a decadent, violent, restless population is seen courting disaster. In the other, a Garden of Eden full of innocents stays blithely unaware, until it is too late, of the imminence and magnitude of the Fall. In our age it is the latter view which has generally held sway. We have sympathized with the young against the old, with those who fought against those who stayed at home. The aura of doomed innocence still clings to the unsuspecting heads of those young volunteers of 1914. It seems to us their most striking quality, still retaining its power to move us though sixty odd years have intervened. The legendary innocence of 1914 youth has become indissolubly part of the pre-war summer, the last peacetime summer in which they flourished undisturbed. 'They were the last of our English youth,' claimed Pound, writing in the 1960's, 'to be brought up in a state of innocence. The ironic gods never had more wicked sport with any generation.'

Yet to many of those who lived through 1914, unable to reconcile their happy memories of it with their unhappy memories of what came afterwards, it has seemed looking back that, as Lord Boothby put it, even though 'the summer was glorious . . . distant thunder muttered' in the air. Somehow, they feel, even if it was buried deep in their subconscious, they ought to have known that the air heavy with the scents of summer, was poisoned, that worms had burrowed a trail into the ripening apples. With hindsight Boothby attaches importance to the fact that, as an Eton schoolboy, he slept that summer with the slim volume of Housman's *A Shropshire Lad* on the table beside his bed. He had, he says, turned down the page at the following poem:

On the idle hill of summer,
   Sleepy with the flow of streams,
Far I hear the steady drummer
   Drumming like a noise in dreams.

Far and near and low and louder
   On the roads of earth go by,
Dear to friends and food for powder
   Soldiers marching, all to die.

East and West on fields forgotten
   Bleach the bones of comrades slain,
Lovely lads and dead and rotten:
   None that go return again.

Later on he was introduced at the Eton and Harrow cricket match at Lords to 'a small man, with alert and kindly eyes'. 'Take a good look at him,' Boothby remembers his father saying, 'because you will hear of him again.' Two weeks later, Lord Jellicoe was commanding the British Fleet at war.

In the same way the death of a young man before the war is seen as an ominous harbinger of the many deaths that would follow. The accidental drowning of Denis Anson beside a boat full of partying young people on the Thames in early July is described by Rupert Hart-Davis, whose mother Sibbie was one of the guests, as 'a tragedy appalling enough at the time' but moreover a foretaste of the bereavements which would become commonplace afterwards. Looking back on July 1914 it seemed to Vera Brittain that 'an ominous stillness, an atmosphere of brooding expectation' hung over those radiant days. Or was it simply that it was hard, especially for those who went through the hell of 1914–1918, to accept that four years of such injurious malevolence could be preceded by anything which smacked of a golden age? 'They were gay and happy days,' wrote Nancy Astor, 'but all the time the shadow was there . . .' '[It] moved with us everywhere we went,' echoed Osbert Sitwell in his memoirs of the pre-war period, 'growing and darkening' inexorably. 'Something was going wrong in the world, and could surely be felt by the sensitive, through the intense sweetness of being alive at that time . . .'

The decay that is supposed to have afflicted England before 1914, sapping her spirit, 'loosening the fibres', turning her, thought some, into a decadent paradise for hedonists, made war (given England's weakness and Germany's military ambitions and growing military strength) seem to them not only likely but inevitable. In the last years before the war right-wingers such as Feiling, writing in 1913 his *Toryism: A Political Dialogue*, saw all around them the signs of decay. He was, he felt, witnessing the death-throes of a once-great empire which like the Roman Empire was sinking giggling into a sea of its own sloth and greed. The pointers he lists seem irrelevant now: 'Towns instead of country . . . machinery instead of men, imported food supplies and exported harvest hands, a mercenary army, a navy withdrawn from the frontier of Empire to defend its heart, crushing taxation on the producers of wealth, faith dim and luxury gross . . .' But his pessimism was real, and others shared it. Osbert Sitwell, writing of London before the war, called it the West End of the world. 'All the trade, all the benefits of exploitation, flowed in to enrich it . . . [with] luxury goods . . . Material improvement alone was of consequence . . .' In July 1914 a John Galsworthy piece appeared in *The Nation* under the heading 'Studies of Extravagance: The Latest Thing'. It condemned an age which 'ran all the time, without any foolish notion where it was running to', an age which had been 'born to dance the moon down, to ragtime', an age without a soul.

All round them the merchants of doom found evidence of moral and national decay. They found it in the 'dastardly outrages' of those 'frenzied criminals', the suffragettes, to whom nothing was sacred, and who burnt down churches and disrupted Buckingham Palace garden-parties with the same callous disregard 'for God and man'.

They found it in the first tentative stirrings of that sleeping giant, the labour movement, whose unions, newly confident of their legality, stood ready in 1914, to flex their collective bargaining muscles. With the knowledge of their power, came a new spirit of egalitarianism. Entrenched attitudes towards class and behaviour were being challenged. Virginia Woolf, looking back on the pre-war period, in 1924, saw a change in attitudes already visible and 'when human relationships change,' she deduced, 'changes in religion, conduct, art, politics and literature are inevitable.' To her such changes, which were to emerge much more vividly over the course of the war, had already been set in motion. 'All human relationships have shifted,' she wrote of the era before war broke out, '. . . between masters and servants, husbands and wives, parents and children . . .

The first signs of it are recorded in the books of Samuel Butler: the plays of Bernard Shaw continue to record it. In life one can see the change, if I may use a homely illustration, in the character of one's cook. The Victorian cook lived like a leviathan in the lower depths, formidable, silent, obscure, inscrutable; the Georgian cook is a creature of sunshine and fresh air; in and out of the drawing-room, now to borrow the *Daily Herald*, now to ask advice about a hat . . .'

The London society hostess, insensible of the feelings of her domestics – let alone her cook's taste in hats – bemoaned instead the state of social flux which had afflicted even the hallowed London Season, as the new-rich middle classes knocked at Society's door. 'Hostesses are making a stand,' sniffed the *Manchester Guardian* social column in June 8, '. . . the thing has reached [such] a pitch . . . One no longer entertains those one wants, but those who want to come.' Unimportant, even trivial perhaps, but in such things as these, the older generation saw the breaking up of the old order, the crumbling of the way of life they knew.

The progressives among the young were in revolt against the Victorian age. More than anything, they yearned to be modern, to shake off the rigid social conventions and stifling formality which had governed their parents' generation. The politics of Ruskin and the Webbs, the art of Roger Fry, the 'raw-meat designs' of Wyndham Lewis, the plays of Ibsen and George Bernard Shaw, the futuristic visions of H. G. Wells – all had provoked a new freedom of discussion. Arnold Bennett and H. G. Wells were writing to break the conspiracy of silence about sex. Dostoyevsky was the favoured reading among Oxford undergraduates, while Conrad's *Chance* with its preoccupation about the role of women, was one of the fashionable novels of the year. In 1912 the first volume of *Georgian Poetry* had been published: everything it stood for was a denial of Victorian romanticism. 'To be a poet is to be frank even unto brutality,' decided one enthusiastic critic. Frankness, easy manners, informality were the hallmarks of the new age.

A host of artists flocked to London, opened studios and set about living out the bohemian life. Violet Hunt who 'went the pace' among them, later looked back with some amazement on those 'flurried years', spent cabbing hither and thither in a whirlwind of nervous gaiety, then 'lying awake from an excess of fatigue'. 'Cubes, pets, protégés, dinners and dances, the latest in everything; clothes, books, plays, pictures and ideas! . . . We were poised on the point of a needle, trembling in space . . .'

The coming of ragtime from the United States, and the accompanying craze for dances like the 'bunny hug', 'chicken scramble' and 'turkey trot' paved the way for easier relations between the sexes. So did the latest feminine fashions, which liberated women from the hour-glass curves of Edwardian clothes and set them free in straight, short dresses and brighter colours. *Punch* in July 1914 was grumbling about the increasing use of cosmetics and the 'scandalous brevity of female bathing-attire'. 'I can't find my bathing-dress anywhere,' said a female cartoon-character in the July 8 issue, to which her husband replied, 'See if you've got it on.'

Richard Aldington, one of the survivors of the Western Front, whose novel *Death of a Hero*, published in 1929, was a violent attack on the senselessness of the slaughter, sent his hero, George Winterbourne, into a passionate physical love affair in the summer before the war as pointedly as he sent him to an heroic death in the month of the Armistice. The young men and women of 1914 whom his hero was supposed to represent, were, he says, in revolt against pre-Raphaelite and Tennysonian idealism 'which made love a sort of hand-holding in the Hesperides'. Freud was as yet scarcely known in 1914. His *Interpretation of Dreams*, published the year before, was to be circulated, according to the publishers' note, among doctors, clerics, academics and lawyers only. And so, Aldington claims, his generation rediscovered for themselves the importance of physical love. In an attempt to counter the unhappy influence of Victorian and Edwardian prudishness and ignorance, Aldington's characters discuss such formerly forbidden topics as birth-control, and earnestly pass around for reading a book with the daring title, *The Psychology of Sex*.

George Winterbourne was an unconventional hero, that is certain, but he was not too far ahead of his time. In 1914 the London Galton Eugenics Laboratory announced a survey showing that mechanical contraceptive devices were in use among the working-class. The coverage afforded this item in the newspapers was one proof that the wall of silence surrounding any mention of bodily functions, and hitherto preventing the airing of genuine sexual problems, had at last been breached. 'Everybody was the architect of a New Jerusalem,' claimed Aldington of 1914 England. The younger generation particularly was 'swarming with ideas of social reform'. To the defenders of the old order, still clinging to the beliefs and tenets of the Victorian age, the war came as a simplification if not exactly as a relief. Before August 1914, faced with the aimless restlessness, the collective impatience that characterized the last long, hot stillness before the storm, they longed for simplicity, for release from uncertainty and tension, for a return to the old, familiar ways. Now that war was inevitable, at least they could recognize the enemy they fought. Instead of the shadowy forces of progress, they saw opposite them the flesh-and-blood soldiers of the Hun. Surely in the face of a common foe, in a country united to such solemn purpose, there would be a chance for national regeneration; for ending the downhill slide; for a purging, as Richard Aldington wrote after the war with conscious irony, 'from the vices supposed to be engendered by peace'. 'Purged and ennobled', he continued bitterly, 'by slaughter and lice, [we] were to beget a race of even nobler fellows.'

After the war in all its horror was over, there were those, like the novelist Stefan Zweig, who would blame 'a surplus force . . . a tragic . . . dynamism that . . . sought violent release'. Or they would conclude, as Churchill did of 1914, that 'there was a strange temper in the air. Almost one might think the world wished to suffer.' The Tommies in the trenches, and their young officers like Wilfred Owen, Robert Graves and Siegfried Sassoon who viewed these vile surroundings and the ever-increasing casualty lists with bitter cynicism and anger, had no such scruples in apportioning blame.

Graves's irreverent, iconoclastic *Goodbye to All That* and Richard Aldington's impassioned diatribe masquerading as a novel, *Death of a Hero*, came out in 1929 along with twenty-seven other war books. The tone of each of these two was very different, but they were united in one common view: each claimed that his generation was duped into war by what Graves, in a letter to the *Times Literary Supplement*, referred to as 'lying propaganda and a campaign of organised blood lust'. 'It was the regime of Cant *before* the War,' accused Aldington, 'which made the Cant *during* the War so damnably possible and easy. On our coming of age the Victorians generously handed us a charming little cheque for fifty guineas – and fifty-one months of hell . . .' Aldington equated civilian enthusiasm for the war with what he called the 'minor gentry, kicked-backside-of-the-empire code'. His hero, George Winterbourne, experienced this at first hand in his minor Edwardian public school, whose aim was to turn out '*real* boys ... thoroughly manly fellows ... the empire's backbone ... We prepare for the Universities of course, but our pride is our excellent Sports Record' – that and the OTC. France, for Winterbourne, is merely a continuation of this 'Kipling-esque Empire' training. The Staff Officers address the subalterns as OTC sergeants addressed the school. 'You are the war generation. You were born to fight this war, and it's got to be won ... So make up your minds to it.'

Winterbourne's experiences are fictional of course, but many pre-First World War schoolboys resented the downgrading of scholarship then prevalent in the public school system, and the worship of sport. From his first moment at Charterhouse Robert Graves suffered an intense 'oppression of spirit': as a scholar ignored and despised by six hundred games-mad boys, he felt 'out of a different sack from the rest'. Leonard Woolf, on the other hand, was 'sufficiently good at games to make intelligence and hard work pass as an eccentricity instead of being chastised as vice or personal nastiness'. Not all of those who went through the Edwardian school system were as brutally critical of it as the seventeen-year-old Alec Waugh, whose novel of public school life in 1915, *The Loom of Youth*, created a stir immediately after the war. Overshadowed as his school life was by the 'tyranny of the bloods', Waugh's memories of those days were bleak. 'You may drudge at games,' he recalled, 'that is commendable; but to drudge at the acquisition of knowledge is pitiable, and not to be endured.' As a result, he concluded, the public school man, his sights set on sport and adventure, had never learnt to think: a fact which 'fairly helped,' Waugh observed caustically, 'to get us out of the mess of August 1914'.

Jonathan Gathorne-Hardy in his interesting study of *The Public School Phenomenon* has paid tribute to the skill with which the late Victorian and Edwardian schools 'whirl[ed] school loyalty, patriot-ism, games, God, the [monarch], the headmaster, team spirit and nostalgia into one great, intoxicating, sentimental, muddled and inflaming brew'. This was the spirit which walked abroad in 1914, and in August 1914 walked straight into the recruiting-offices. Loyalty to the house and school fostered a wider, national loyalty. The desire to serve the Empire was intense: at Cheltenham the language school, which included Sanskrit and Hindustani, was housed in a bigger building than the Classics Department. At school, games and the Corps harnessed this eager loyalty for the benefit of house or team, but the implication was clear and many masters seem to have believed it: a good rugger training would equip mind, body and character for almost any eventuality in the world outside, including that nebulous circumstance much referred to by Lord Roberts on public school speech-days, 'leadership of men'. It might even, as one distinguished soldier pointed out when addressing a school, teach boys to decide quickly, 'quicker than a company commander with his line of skirmishers in the field'.

A more direct link between sport and war had been forged by Haig's friend and Clifton College schoolfellow Sir Henry Newbolt, whose patriotic poem *Vitaii Lampada* was well known to public schoolboys long before 1914. The first verse tells of a cricket 'blood' playing for the School Eleven:

> There's a breathless hush in the Close tonight –
> Ten to make and match to win –
> A bumping pitch and a blinding light,
> An hour to play and the last man in.
> And it's not for the sake of a ribboned coat,
> Or the selfish hope of a season's fame,
> But his Captain's hand on his shoulder smote –
> "Play up! play up! and play the game!"

In later years far away out in the colonies, the former schoolboy, his back to the wall, is fighting for his life:

> The sand of the desert is sodden red –
> Red with the wreck of a square that broke;
> The Gatling's jammed and the Colonel dead,
> And the regiment blind with dust and smoke;
> The river of death has brimmed his banks,
> And England's far, and Honour a name;
> But the voice of a schoolboy rallies the ranks:
> "Play up! play up! and play the game!"

A poem in *The Times* in August 1914 urging youths to

> 'Put the old blazer and cap away –
> England's colours await your brow'

was doing no more than following in this tradition.

The philistinism in English public schools – Ulric Nisbet in five years at Marlborough never had an afternoon free of games to see

Avebury and Silbury 'twenty minutes from the school gates' – confined schoolboy reading to such well-tried favourites as Buchan, Galsworthy and the P. G. Wodehouse adventure novels. In books like these, or in Hector Hugh Munro's novels for example, the ex-public-school hero sails through a host of manly adventures to root out the sort of slackers, crooks and rotters who let down the tone of England, just as in yesteryears they must have let down the tone of the school. The prizing of adventure for its own sake and the assumption that for an Englishman nothing could ever go wrong to part him from his heroic destiny, must have encouraged a taste for glory in generations of English schoolboys before 1914. George Orwell summed up the public school attitude as follows: 'The King is on his throne and the pound is worth a pound. Over in Europe the comic foreigners are jabbering and gesticulating, but the grim, grey battleships of the British fleet are steaming up the Channel and at the outposts of Empire the monocled Englishmen are holding the niggers at bay . . . Everything is safe, solid and unquestionable. Everything will be the same for ever and ever.'

No wonder that when war broke out, Julian Grenfell talked blithely, as though it were enough, of 'throwing stones at the Germans'; while Osbert Sitwell saw his fellow Guards officers instruct their servants to pack evening clothes for Berlin. And no wonder, given their unshakeable confidence in the Empire's underlying security, that so many seized the chance in the summer of 1914 to experience what seemed bound to be an exciting, if brief, adventure. J. B. Priestley remembered it as 'a challenge to what we felt was our untested manhood' that came out of 'the unclouded blue of that summer . . . Other men, who had not lived as easily as we had, had drilled and marched and borne arms – couldn't we? We too could leave home and soft beds and the girls to soldier for a while . . .' 'It is awful for R. being kept at Harrow while this is going on,' wrote a seventeen-year-old midshipman in 1914 to his mother, a friend of Lady Desborough. 'I have written to try and cheer him up by saying the war is certain to last two years, by which time he will be able to join in. I do hope you and Father will tell him this too, whatever you may think.'

Robert Nichols, an Oxford undergraduate of 1914 who joined up in his long vacation along with thousands of others, made a list after the war, of the motives which had emptied the Oxford quadrangles. Along with the usual, typically hazy notions of 'honour' and 'suffering', he was honest enough to include a 'vague feeling that it was "the thing to do"'. Here the public school ethos can be seen most successfully at work. In the years before 1914 it turned out what would prove ideal officer material in the First World War: men who were loyal, decent, trusting, unimaginative and totally conformist. Individuality, like aestheticism, was viewed with suspicion and distaste by both boys and masters. And the parents agreed. Osbert Sitwell, instead of going to Oxford as he had hoped, was sent into the Army by his father to knock all the silly artistic nonsense out of his head. The uniform and strict hierarchical structure of his public school had prepared him well for it.

Rules and customs, traditions and rituals, governed every minute of the pre-war schoolboy's day, enforcing from him a strict conformity. 'How to wear a hat,' Gathorne-Hardy lists. 'How far to turn up your trousers; how to walk down stairs; how to walk when a blood, when not a blood, when with blood . . .' Often there was a private school vocabulary to be observed as well. At school these privileged boys learnt the passwords to a future of privilege; the desired behaviour at Henley or Ascot; the correct accent; proper titles to use; suitable views. As well as loyalty to the school they absorbed a tribal loyalty to their class. And thus, when the call to arms came, they flocked to answer it like a school roll-call. They were doing what they had been taught, by sport and by their masters. They were playing the game as a team. The only difference, as they saw it, was that this time they were wearing the colours of their country, instead of those of their house or their school.

'That is the faith of the Public School Boy,' scoffed Alec Waugh in 1915, "which except he believe he cannot be saved . . ." [He] is slack, easy-going, tolerant . . . laughs at good things, smiles at bad . . . has learnt to do what he is told.' Considering what became of their predecessors, it is perhaps not surprising that the post-war generation at English public schools reacted as strongly as it did. At Lancing after the war, according to Alec Waugh's more famous brother Evelyn, the OTC was derided as a joke. At Eton the boys of one house that Anthony Powell remembers appeared on parade in horn-rimmed glasses, counted off one to ten and then continued, 'Knave, queen, king, ace'.

The post-war young blamed the Old Men for the war. They had taken the country into it; they had duped their sons into joining it; they had exploited their bravery and idealism; they had watched them die. The war came to be seen as a catastrophe visited on innocent young heads by the 'stupidity and self-protective alarm' of the older generation. In 1917 while in hospital, Robert Graves had fantasized about a war fought only by those over forty-five. 'Well, dear father,' his imaginary youth told the middle-aged soldier, 'how proud I am of you serving your country . . . prepared to make even the supreme sacrifice! I only wish I were your age: how willingly would I buckle on my armour . . . As it is, of course, I can't be spared; I have to stay behind at the War Office and administrate for you lucky old men.' Reading Sassoon's poems in 1921, Sir Henry Newbolt struck out indignantly at 'Owen and the rest of the broken men [who] rail at the Old Men who sent the young to die: they have suffered cruelly, but in the nerves and not the heart . . . Paternity apart, what Englishman of fifty wouldn't far rather stop the shot himself than see the boys do it for him.' He gained little sympathy either from those who had survived the war or from their younger brothers. George Orwell, who in 1914 had a patriotic poem *Awake! Young Men of England* published in the *Henley and South Oxfordshire Standard*, chronicled his generation's change of heart. 'Throughout the whole nation,' he wrote of the years after the war, 'there was running a wave of revolutionary feeling . . . It was a revolt of youth against age, resulting directly from the war . . . By 1918 everyone under forty was in a bad temper with his elders, and the mood of anti-militarism which followed naturally upon the fighting was extended into a general revolt against orthodoxy and authority. At that time there was, among the young, a curious cult of hatred of "old men". The dominance of "old men" was held to be responsible for every evil known to humanity, and every accepted institution from Scott's novels to the House of Lords was derided because "old men" were in favour of it . . .' Derided too were patriotic sentiments of the kind which youth had expressed in 1914, and 'old men' applauded: of the kind which Rupert Brooke had voiced in his sonnet *Peace*. One of five poems grouped under the title *1914*, it had portrayed him as glad to leave

> '. . . a world grown old and cold and weary,
> Leave the sick hearts that honour could not move,
> And half-men, and their dirty songs and dreary,
> And all the little emptiness of love!'

Brooke died in 1915 of blood poisoning caused by a gnat bite on the way to Gallipoli, with only a few nights spent on active service, and never having been tested in a major battle. His acquaintance with danger was slight. It amounted to standing guard in the courtyard of a Belgian château while his men slept and in the far distance German soldiers marched, and Antwerp burned. His division then returned to England. The stirring *1914* sonnets were written from the mundane safety of a training camp. Later on, when they had become famous and Brooke was a public figure, symbol of 'the nobility of our youth' to patriotic civilian England, Winston Churchill would have to use all his skill in *The Times* obituary to skirt round the inescapable but somewhat ignominious truth that the hero of the war sonnets had never really been to war. 'He expected to die ... he was willing to die,' stressed Churchill, and 'the last few months of his life [were] months of preparation in gallant comradeship and open air ... the poet soldier ... advanced towards the brink in perfect serenity, with absolute conviction of the rightness of his country's cause ...'

Brooke's fellow poet-soldiers had little sympathy for the patriotic poses struck by a hero who had never wallowed in mud at the foot of a trench, or waited sick to his stomach to go over the top at dawn. Charles Sorley, the twenty-year-old ex-Marlburian schoolboy killed at Loos, whom John Masefield considered the most promising of the war poets, had his own wry epitaph for Brooke. 'I saw Rupert Brooke's death in the *Morning Post*,' he wrote. 'The *Morning Post*, which has always hitherto disapproved of him, is now loud in his praises because he had conformed to their stupid axiom of literary criticism that the only stuff of poetry is violent physical experience, by dying on active service.' Of Brooke himself he said, 'He is far too obsessed with his own sacrifice, regarding the going to war of himself (and others) as a highly intense, remarkable and sacrificial exploit, whereas it is merely the conduct demanded of him (and others) by the turn of circumstances, where non-compliance with this demand would have made life intolerable.' Edmund Blunden, Sassoon's friend, later spoke out more bluntly. 'That Brooke, he exclaimed, 'if he had lived to march into the horrifying battlefields of the River Ancre with his surviving companions of the Hood Battalion in the deep winter of 1916, would have continued to write sonnets or other poems in the spirit of the 1914 sonnets, is something I cannot credit.' Brooke's much vaunted patriotism, concluded Sorley, was nothing more than a 'sentimental attitude'.

It was as hapless victims that the post-war survivors saw themselves: victims of time, of place, of history, victims of the heartless mistakes of an older generation, but most of all, as victims of their own 'primal innocence' in August 1914. *The War Generation: Ave* is the title prefacing Vera Brittain's *Testament of Youth*, in which she sees 'a generation grow to flower' with 'dreams of happiness we thought secure', while 'imminent and fierce outside the door', fate waits to steal their youth and sour their innocence. 'We didn't think of ourselves as different,' Ulric Nisbet says, looking back on his contemporaries of 1914. 'We were *just* different. We were innocent. We were very simple people.' 'A harmless young shepherd in a soldier's coat,' Edmund Blunden pictured himself in his memoir *Undertones of War*. Siegfried Sassoon, pedalling on July 31 the thirty miles from Rye to Weirleigh through his beloved Kentish Weald, imagined the orchards and oast-houses and hop-kilns burnt and plundered as he passed along the dusty lanes criss-crossing the English countryside. He resolved that 'when the Germans arrived' he would have a gun in his hand 'even if I didn't know how to fire it properly'. But despite this instinctive impulse to defend the Weald – 'the world of my youngness' – the idea of war then in 1914 seemed to him as absurd and unreasonable as the idea of fighting over again the Wars of the Roses.

Blunden's self-image of innocent English youth is reinforced by the memory cherished of him by a fellow-officer. Eighteen in 1914, he joined the Royal Sussex Regiment, one of its youngest lieutenants, the following year, and was in France for the ominous build-up to the Battle of the Somme. 'I was not anxious to go,' he begins his war memoirs, and adds ingenuously: 'There was something about France in those days which looked to me, despite all journalistic enchanters, to be dangerous.' But go he did and Guy Chapman welcomed 'a very young, very fair and very shy subaltern' to the trenches. He took his leave of Blunden carrying a slim, paper-covered volume entitled *The Harbingers, Poems by E. C. Blunden*, written, some of them, at Oxford before the war and described by Paul Fussell as Georgian and exactly reflecting their author's character: 'shy, modest ... gentle, courteous and a bit dreamy'.

On June 30 1916, the day before the infamous first day of the

Somme, the Royal Sussex took part in a diversionary attack near La Bassée to draw the German fire. 'Like a butcher's shop,' a soldier later described it, and Blunden wrote of his own trenches being 'knocked silly'. Yet the picture of Blunden ('Rabbit' or 'Bunny' as he was nicknamed) never entirely changes. 'What an age since 1914!' he sighs, but two years later after 'the bitterness of waste' at Ypres and Hamel and Thiepval's 'lunatical wood', he is able, as he leaves the war for ever, to be 'filled with this simple joy. I might have known the war by this time, but I was still too young to know its depth of ironic cruelty.'

Sassoon harboured more complex motives for proclaiming as he did his pre-war 'innocence'. Furthermore, as an English country gentleman brought up in affluence far more comfortably than the schoolmaster's son Edmund Blunden, there were more contrasts he could draw between his idyllic life in a pre-war Eden and 'death's grey land' where 'nothing blossoms but the sky'. At Weirleigh Sassoon had played as a child amidst the leafy greenness of apple and cherry orchards. His memories of adolescence – a protracted adolescence enjoyed until he was twenty-eight on the eve of war – were untroubled ones. He recalls well-schooled horses; 'faithful', solicitous family servants; even the hop-pickers down from the slums of London were 'merry', and 'strains of the concertina or accordion' wafted on summer evenings across the fields. Sassoon hunted in winter; played tennis on the court below the lawn at Weirleigh on summer evenings (first having dug up all the dandelion roots with his artistic mother's palette knife); and spent 'long days of dry weather' playing cricket with 'white figures moving to and fro on green grounds'.

His relationship with his mother, too, was a happy and secure one. Coming from a family with literary and artistic connections herself (Sassoon's uncle was the sculpture Sir Hamo Thornycroft and another well known relative the literateur Edmund Gosse), she had encouraged her son's poetry ever since he solemnly presented his first volume of poems to her at the age of eleven. Sassoon's leisured, pastoral pre-war life was reflected in his verse. 'No poet of twentieth century England . . .' stated Edmund Blunden later, 'was originally more romantic and floral than young Siegfried Sassoon from Kent.'

Sassoon joined the Sussex Yeomanry as a trooper in August 1914 two days before the declaration of war. The first few months of training which began his military service proved 'a mounted infantry picnic in perfect weather' as August and September rolled on under 'hot blue skies'. There was 'sadness in the sunshine' as news came of the Retreat from Mons and the Battle of the Marne, but no real hint as yet of how rudely his life would change. On the contrary, he was thrilled to be on a horse again: it was just like his hunting days. He was even riding his own mount, mobilized on the outbreak of war and sold to the Government for fifty pounds.

Sassoon makes a deliberately vivid contrast between these 'idyllic early weeks' spent zestfully out of doors 'in abounding health' and seeming to him almost a continuation of his pre-war country life; and the life in France, 'where all is ruin' with 'sad, smoking, flat horizons, reeking woods', 'dulled sunken faces', 'haggard and hopeless men'. In his heavily autobiographical *Memoirs of George Sherston*, the gory brutality of the *Memoirs of an Infantry Officer* follows the peaceful, pastoral *Memoirs of a Fox-hunting Man*. From an eager volunteer in 1914 with a belief in his cause and 'aspirations to heroism', Sassoon reversed his attitude completely in 1916 and, as Edmund Blunden described it, waged 'a splendid war on the War'. The turning-point came in the month of the Somme. Having watched 'Armageddon' unfold before his eyes, he was invalided home to civilian England. Here, besides reading patriotic euphemisms about the Somme in the daily press, he had to come to terms with a complete lack of understanding about the war in the older family members. 'No explanation of mine could ever reach [them],' he wrote later in *Siegfried's Journey*. 'They weren't capable of wanting to know the truth.' His uncle Hamo Thornycroft even compared his war service, 'well and truly accomplished', to a seventeenth-century water clock.

Sassoon determined that the world should know the truth about the war. He turned his back on his early poems (inspired by Brooke and celebrating the Army's 'happy legions') and went on with increasingly angry accuracy to record the 'place rotten with death', the 'plastering slime', the 'snoring weary men' that he saw around him. In September 1916 he went to stay with Lady Ottoline Morrell at Garsington and met among her circle many of the best known arch-enemies of the war. One of her friends, Bertrand Russell, would in 1917 help Sassoon compose his anti-war statement, *A Soldier's Declaration*. As 'a soldier convinced that . . . [he was] acting on behalf of soldiers', Sassoon stated that he believed the war was being prolonged by those who had the power to end it. For reasons which were 'evil and unjust', for 'political errors and insincerities', the troops were being sacrificed; while at home the majority of the population watched their agonies with 'callous complacency'. For Sassoon, too, the war had become a bad joke played by their elders on the young soldiers at the Front.

Sassoon, like many of those who would come to write about the war, saw himself as a soldier-victim, and as such played up the innocence with which he went to sacrifice. His pre-war self, in the fictional guise of George Sherston, is seen 'mooning' about the Kentish countryside, attending cricket matches which were 'an evocation of all that was peaceful in my past'. On the morning of the Flower Show Cricket Match he wakes at dawn and stares out at the tree-tops, anticipating a 'pleasantly eventful day' – an ironic parallel with the many dawns he would later spend standing to in the trenches, staring across no man's land in fear of an attack. 'How little I knew of the enormous world beyond [this] valley,' Sassoon/ Sherston thinks as he looks out over the familiar Kent landscape, conveniently forgetting his own education or his mother's influential friends. While training for war in the late summer of 1914, Sassoon feels 'almost as if I had been waiting for this thing to happen', but his role he sees as that of victim, 'obscure and submissive'. Such passivity does not tie in well with the front line image he was to gain as the bold, brave officer, 'Mad Jack', who single-handedly took and held an enemy trench, fired with the desire to 'kill someone at close quarters'.

Nor is Sassoon consistent in his portrayal of his life before August 1914 as an uninterrupted paradise. There was a serpent in his Eden which, as he admitted in moments of honesty, had nothing to do with the coming war. Sassoon envied Rupert Brooke for the skill with which Brooke cultivated the image of a poet and Cambridge intellectual and yet retained his reputation as a public school sporting man, who had once played cricket and football for Rugby. Sassoon felt his own life was split in two: he had separate existences, sporting and literary. Neither satisfied him fully; in neither did he feel entirely at home; and certainly neither gave him the material he so badly needed in order to write. The war when it came on August 4 rescued Sassoon from a slough of boredom and gloom. Later, despite its horrors, it set his pen racing. 'The tragic turn on events which changed the world,' he writes of August 1914 in *The Weald of*

Youth, 'was about to take the trivial personal problems off [my] hands and set [me] on the road to unexpected success.'

Nevertheless, for Sassoon as for the others who were emerging alongside him as the new generation of war poets, the shattering experience of trench warfare distorted their image of life before the war and poisoned their memories of August 4. Whereas Rupert Brooke's *1914* sonnets offered up his youth as a willing sacrifice to England, Isaac Rosenberg's conclusion in his poem *August 1914* a few years later, was that he had been robbed of his youth.

> Three lives hath one life –
> Iron, honey, gold.
> The gold, the honey gone –
> Left is the hard and cold.
>
> Iron are our lives
> Molten right through our youth.
> A burnt space through ripe fields
> A fair mouth's broken tooth.

Compared with the hard and cold of trench squalor and drudgery, the idea of 'before the war', of youthful pleasures, of peacetime, began to glisten like gold, and taste in retrospect as sweet as honey. In 1917, while in Craiglockhart War Hospital, Wilfred Owen transformed some pre-war jottings, *From My Diary, July 1914*, into an evocation of that last summer, seen now as a youthful idyll, gone for ever. He recalled,

> Boys
>   Bursting through the surface of the ebony pond.
> Flashes
>   Of swimmers carving through the sparkling cold.
> Flashes
>   Gleaming with wetness to the morning gold.

In *The Last Day of Leave*, a poem written and set during the war but looking back on better days in peacetime, Robert Graves asked nostalgically,

> Do you remember the lily lake?
> We were all there, all five of us in love,
> Not one yet killed, widowed or broken hearted . . .

The memory summoned up is one of innocence before the Fall. Already, even during the war, the legend of a pre-war lost Eden was being created.

It is a legend that has survived, that has taken hold of our sympathy and imagination, despite sixty odd years of iconoclasm, during which other legends have been shattered and other myths decried. 'The spring of 1914,' says George Bowling in George Orwell's 1930's novel *Coming Up For Air*. 'People then had something that we haven't got now.' Kenneth Allsop, in his book about the 1950's, *The Angry Decade*, felt he was speaking for his generation, 'a great many [of whom] have an intense longing for the security and the innocence that seems to have been present in Britain before the 1914 war'. Nearer to our own time, Philip Larkin evokes this innocence in his 1964 poem *MCMXIV* (1914). He recreates a scene which, although we could not have been there, still seems utterly familiar to us. We know

> Those long uneven lines
> Standing . . . patiently . . .
> Grinning as if it were all
> An August Bank Holiday lark . . .

We know what they were like:

> Never such innocence,
> Never before or since,
> As changed itself to past
> Without a word – the men
> Leaving the gardens tidy,
> The thousands of marriages
> Lasting a little while longer:
> Never such innocence again.

And we know, for it is part of the myth, that such times and such people will never come again.

BIBLIOGRAPHY

Aldin, Cecil *Time I Was Dead* (Eyre & Spottiswoode, 1934)
Aldington, Richard *Death of a Hero* (Chatto & Windus, 1929)
Allsop, Kenneth *The Angry Decade* (Peter Owen, 1958)
Asquith, Cynthia *Haply I May Remember*
  Remember And Be Glad (Barrie, 1952)
Asquith, Herbert *Moments of Memory* (Hutchinson, 1937)
Asquith, Margot *More Memories* (Cassell, 1933)

Bailey, Leslie *Leslie Bailey's BBC Scrapbooks*, Vol. 1 1896–1914
  (BBC, 1966)
Bedford, Sybille *Aldous Huxley*, Vol. 1 (Chatto & Windus, 1973)
Blunden, Edmund *Undertones of War* (Sanderson, 1928)
Blythe, Ronald *The View in Winter* (Allen Lane, 1979)
Boothby, Robert J. *Recollections of a Rebel* (Hutchinson, 1978)
Brittain, Vera *Testament of Youth* (Gollancz, 1933)
Brown, Malcolm *Tommy Goes to War* (Dent, 1978)
Buchan, John *Francis & Riversdale Grenfell, A Memoir* (Thomas
  Nelson, 1920)

Cameron, James *1914* (Cassell, 1959)
Cassar, George H. *Kitchener* (William Kimber, 1977)
Churchill, Winston S. *The World Crisis, 1911–14* (Butterworth,
  1923)
Clark, Kenneth *Another Part of the Wood* (John Murray, 1974)
Cooper, Diana *The Rainbow Comes And Goes* (Hart-Davis, 1958)
Cooper, Duff *Old Men Forget* (Hart-Davis, 1953)

Dangerfield, George *The Strange Death of Liberal England*
  (MacGibbon & Kee, 1966)

Deghy, Guy & Keith Weaterhouse   *Café Royal* (Hutchinson, 1955)
Donaldson, Frances   *Edward VIII* (Weidenfeld & Nicolson, 1974)

Eden, Anthony   *Another World* (Allen Lane, 1976)

Fielding, Daphne   *Emerald & Nancy* (Eyre & Spottiswoode, 1968)
Fussell, Paul   *The Great War & Modern Memory* (O.U.P., 1975)

Gardner, Brian (ed)   *Up the Line to Death, The War Poets 1914–18* (Methuen, 1964)
Gathorne-Hardy, Jonathan   *The Public School Phenomenon* (Hodder & Stoughton, 1977)
Graves, Robert   *Goodbye to All That* (Cassell, 1929)

Harrison, Michael   *Rosa* (Peter Davies, 1962)
Hart-Davis, Rupert   *The Arms of Time* (Hamish Hamilton, 1979)
Hassell, Christopher   *Edward Marsh* (Longmans, 1959)
Hassell, Christopher   *Rupert Brooke* (Faber, 1964)
Hastings, Michael   *The Handsomest Young Man in England* (Michael Joseph, 1967)
Hynes, Samuel   *The Edwardian Turn of Mind* (O.U.P., 1968)
Hynes, Samuel   *The Auden Generation* (Faber, 1979)

Jolliffe, John   *Raymond Asquith, Life and Letters* (Collins, 1980)

Keegan, John   *The Face of Battle* (Cape, 1976)
Keynes, Geoffrey (ed)   *The Letters of Rupert Brooke* (Faber, 1968)
Knightley, Philip   *The First Casualty* (Harvest, 1976)
Knox, R.   *Patrick Shaw-Stewart* (Collins, 1920)

Leslie, Anita   *Edwardians in Love* (Hutchinson, 1972)
Leslie, Anita   *Jennie* (Hutchinson, 1969)
Linklater, Eric   *Fanfare for a Tin Hat* (Macmillan, 1970)

Maclaren, Barbara   *Women of the War* (Hodder & Stoughton, 1919)
Macmillan, Harold   *Winds of Change 1914–39* (Macmillan, 1966)
Macmillan, Harold   *The Past Masters* (Macmillan, 1975)

MacMillan, James *The Way We Were 1900–1914* (William
    Kimber, 1978)
Marwick, Arthur *The Deluge* (Macmillan, 1975)
Marwick, Arthur *Women at War 1914–18* (Fontana, 1977)
Marcus, Geoffrey *Before the Lamps Went Out* (Allen & Unwin,
    1965)
Masters, Anthony *Rosa Lewis* (Weidenfeld & Nicolson, 1977)
Meynell, Viola *Julian Grenfell* (Burns & Oates, 1917)
Middlebrook, Martin *First Day on the Somme* (Allen Lane, 1971)
Montague, C. E. *Disenchantment* (Chatto, 1940)
Morrell, Ottoline *Ottoline, The Early Memoirs of Lady Ottoline
    Morrell* (Faber, 1963)
Mosley, Nicholas *Julian Grenfell* (Weidenfeld, 1976)

Ogilvie, Vivian *Our Times* (Batsford, 1953)
Orwell, George *Coming Up for Air* (Secker & Warburg, 1948)
Osborn, E. B. *The New Elizabethans* (Bodley Head, 1919)
Owen, Harold *Journey from Obscurity* (O.U.P., 1965)

Peel, Dorothy *How We Lived Then* (John Lane, 1929)
Playne, Caroline *The Pre-War Mind in Britain* (Allen & Unwin,
    1928)
Playne, Caroline *Society at War 1914–16* (Allen & Unwin, 1931)
Priestley, J. B. *The Edwardians* (Heinemann, 1970)
Pullar, Philippa *Gilded Butterflies* (Hamish Hamilton, 1978)

Quennell, Peter (ed) *Genius in the Drawing-Room* (Weidenfeld &
    Nicolson, 1980)

Read, Donald *Edwardian England 1901–1915* (Harrap, 1972)
Reeves, James (ed) *Georgian Poetry* (Penguin, 1962)
Ribblesdale, Lord *Charles Lister, Letters & Recollections* (Fisher
    Unwin, 1917)

Sassoon, Siegfried *Memoirs of a Fox-Hunting Man* (Faber, 1929)
                    Memoirs of an Infantry Officer (Faber, 1930)
                    The Weald of Youth (Faber, 1942)
Silkin, Jon (ed) *First World War Poetry* (Penguin, 1979)
Sitwell, Osbert *Great Morning* (Macmillan, 1948)

Slater, Guy (ed) *My Warrior Sons* by Arthur C. Borton (Peter Davies, 1973)

Spears, E. L. *Liaison 1914* (Eyre & Spottiswoode, 1968)

Stallworthy, Jon *Wilfred Owen* (Chatto & Windus, 1974)

Sykes, Christopher *Evelyn Waugh* (Collins, 1975)

Sykes, Christopher *Nancy, The Life of Lady Astor* (Collins, 1972)

Taylor, A. J. P. *The First World War, An Illustrated History* (Hamish Hamilton, 1963)

Taylor, A. J. P. *War by Timetable* (Macdonald, 1969)

Terraine, John *Impacts of War, 1914 & 1918* (Hutchinson, 1970)

Thompson, George Malcolm *The Twelve Days, 24 July–August 1914* (Hutchinson, 1964)

Tuchman, Barbara *August 1914* (Constable, 1962)
                 Proud Tower (Hamish Hamilton, 1966)

Turner, E. S. *Dear Old Blighty* (Michael Joseph, 1980)

Waugh, Alec *The Loom of Youth* (Grant Richards, 1918)

Wohl, Robert *The Generation of 1914* (Weidenfeld & Nicolson, 1980)

Woolf, Virginia *Books and Portraits* (Hogarth, 1977)

Ziegler, Philip *Diana Cooper* (Hamish Hamilton, 1981)